Leckie × Leckie

Scotland's leading educational publishers

Advanced Higher
MATHS
PRACTICE QUESTION BOOK

Craig Lowther • Graeme Nolan

Advanced Higher MATHS
PRACTICE QUESTION BOOK

© 2018 Leckie & Leckie Ltd
cover image © Prasert Wongchindawest / Shutterstock.com

001/17052018

10 9 8 7 6 5 4 3 2 1

ISBN 9780008263560

Published by

Leckie & Leckie Ltd

An imprint of HarperCollins Publishers

Westerhill Road, Bishopbriggs, Glasgow, G64 2QT

T: 0844 576 8126   F: 0844 576 8131

leckieandleckie@harpercollins.co.uk   www.leckieandleckie.co.uk

Special thanks to

Jouve (layout and illustration); Ink Tank (cover design);
Project One Publishing Solutions (project management and editing);
Rachel Hamar (answer checking), Philip Bradfield (answer checking),
John Ballantyne (answer checking), Maureen Kennedy (answer checking),
Deirdre Murray (answer checking).

A CIP Catalogue record for this book is available from the
British Library.

Acknowledgements

Whilst every effort has been made to trace the copyright holders, in cases
where this has been unsuccessful, or if any have inadvertently been
overlooked, the Publishers would gladly receive any information
enabling them to rectify any error or omission at the first opportunity.

Printed and bound by CPI Group (UK) Ltd, Croydon, CR0 4YY

How to use this book   **iv**

1	Algebra	1
2	Differentiation	7
3	Integration	17
4	Complex numbers	28
5	Differential equations	37
6	Functions and graphs	46
7	Sequences and series	56
8	Matrices	66
9	Vectors	74
10	Number theory	80
11	Proof	84

ANSWERS
https://collins.co.uk/pages/scottish-curriculum

How to use this book

Welcome to Leckie and Leckie's *Advanced Higher Maths Practice Question Book*. This book follows the structure of the Leckie and Leckie *Advanced Higher Maths Student Book*, so is ideal to use alongside it. Questions have been written to provide practice for topics and concepts which have been identified as challenging for many students.

Examples

Examples with worked solutions provide support for particularly tricky concepts.

Reasoning questions

Questions which require reasoning skills are marked with a ⚙ icon.

Hints

Where appropriate, hints are provided to help give extra guidance and support.

Answers

Check your own work. The answers are provided online at:

https://collins.co.uk/pages/scottish-curriculum

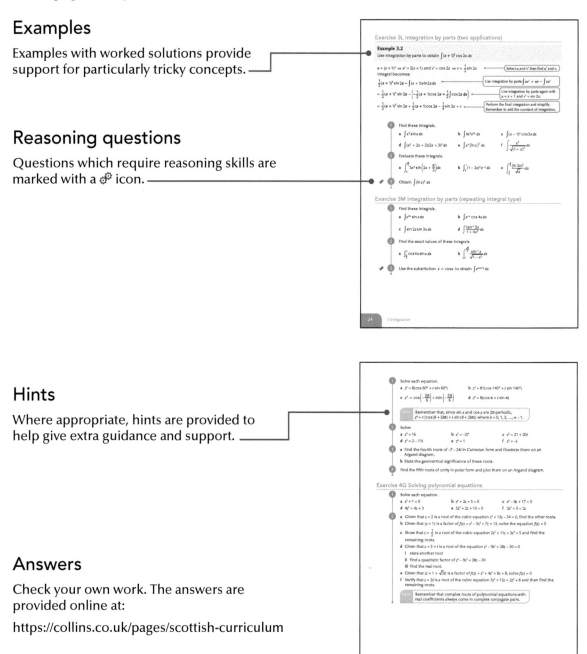

1   Algebra

Exercise 1A Partial fractions (distinct linear factors in denominator)

 Express each in terms of partial fractions.

a $\dfrac{5x + 7}{(x - 1)(x + 3)}$

b $\dfrac{3x + 8}{x(x + 2)}$

c $\dfrac{4 - x}{x^2 + 6x + 8}$

d $\dfrac{2 + 5x}{x^2 - 8x + 7}$

e $\dfrac{5x^2 - 24x - 39}{(x + 1)(2x + 3)(x - 4)}$

f $\dfrac{6}{x^3 - 5x^2 - 4x + 20}$

Exercise 1B Partial fractions (irreducible quadratic factor in denominator)

 Write each expression as a sum of partial fractions.

a $\dfrac{7x^2 + 20x + 12}{(x + 5)(x^2 + 4)}$

b $\dfrac{10}{(x + 2)(x^2 + 2)}$

c $\dfrac{3x^2 + 3x + 2}{x(x^2 + 1)}$

d $\dfrac{2 - x}{x(x^2 + x + 1)}$

e $\dfrac{3x^2 + 9x + 8}{x^3 + x^2 - 2}$

f $\dfrac{3x}{(x + 2)(x^2 + 1)}$

Exercise 1C Partial fractions (repeated linear factor in denominator)

 Find partial fractions for each expression.

a $\dfrac{4x + 17}{(x + 3)^2}$

b $\dfrac{3 - 2x}{x^2 - 4x + 4}$

c $\dfrac{3x^2 + 7x + 1}{x(x + 1)^2}$

d $\dfrac{3 + 2x}{x^2(x - 1)}$

e $\dfrac{2x^2 - 7x + 11}{(x + 3)(x - 2)^2}$

f $\dfrac{1}{x^3 + 3x^2}$

Hint   Remember the extra term when the denominator contains a repeated factor.

Exercise 1D Division of algebraic fractions

Example 1.1

Write $\dfrac{x^3}{x^2 + 2}$ in the form $x + \dfrac{ax}{x^2 + 2}$

$$\begin{array}{r} x \\ x^2 + 2\overline{)\,x^3} \\ \underline{-(x^3 + 2x)} \\ -2x \end{array}$$

Since degree (numerator) $\geqslant$ degree (denominator), divide.

$$\dfrac{x^3}{x^2 + 2} = x - \dfrac{2x}{x^2 + 2}$$

Write the answer in the correct form: quotient + proper algebraic fraction.

Write each improper algebraic fraction as the sum of its quotient and a proper algebraic fraction.

a $\dfrac{2x + 5}{x - 3}$

b $\dfrac{x^2 - 2x + 4}{x^2 + 2}$

c $\dfrac{x^2 - x + 5}{x - 1}$

d $\dfrac{x^3 + 2x - 3}{x^3 + x^2 - x - 2}$

e $\dfrac{x^3}{x^2 - x - 7}$

f $\dfrac{3x^4 + x^3 - 2x^2 + x + 1}{x(x^2 + 2)}$

 A function, f, is defined on suitable real numbers by $f(x) = \dfrac{x^2 - x - 5}{x - 3}$.

a Show that $f(x)$ can be written in the form $x + k + \dfrac{1}{x - 3}$ where k is a constant.

b Hence find the coordinates of the stationary points on the graph of $y = f(x)$.

Exercise 1E Division of algebraic fractions and partial fractions

 Write each algebraic fraction as a quotient and a sum of partial fractions.

a $\dfrac{3x^2 + 4x + 2}{x(x + 1)}$

b $\dfrac{x^2}{x^2 - 4}$

c $\dfrac{5x^2 - 18x + 19}{x^2 - 4x + 4}$

d $\dfrac{4x^3 - 5x^2 - 3x + 2}{x^2(x - 2)}$

e $\dfrac{2x^3 + 5x^2 - 6x + 11}{(x - 1)(x + 3)}$

f $\dfrac{x^4 - x^3 + x^2 - x}{x^3 + x^2 + 3x + 3}$

 Let $f(x) = \dfrac{4x^2 + 3x + 1}{x(x + 1)}$, $x \neq 0, -1$

a Write $f(x)$ as a quotient and a sum of partial fractions.

b Hence find the exact value of $f'(3)$.

Exercise 1F Combinations

 Use your calculator to evaluate the following.

a $4!$

b $8!$

c $0!$

d $^9C_4$

e $^{12}C_8$

f $^{15}C_3$

g $\dbinom{8}{5}$

h $\dbinom{8}{3}$

i $\dbinom{19}{6}$

 Evaluate the following without using a calculator.

a $^6C_3$

b $^{10}C_7$

c $^{17}C_{16}$

d $\dbinom{5}{2}$

e $\dbinom{5}{3}$

f $\dbinom{17}{1}$

3 10 pairs of socks, each with a different design, are in a drawer but none of the socks are paired.

  a How many ways are there of selecting two individual socks from the drawer?

  b What is the probability that two socks, chosen at random, are a matching pair?

  c What is the probability that two socks, chosen at random, are the wearer's favourite pair?

4 A class has 16 fifth year pupils and 12 sixth year pupils.

The teacher is asked to send a group consisting of 2 fifth year pupils and 2 sixth year pupils to the Head Teacher's office.

How many different groups could be selected?

Exercise 1G Properties of $\binom{n}{r}$ and Pascal's triangle

1   **a** **i** Evaluate $^{12}C_7$

     ii Hence write down the value of $^{12}C_5$

  b Copy and complete:

    i $\binom{7}{3} = \binom{7}{\cdots}$
       ii $\binom{12}{11} = \binom{12}{\cdots}$
       iii $\binom{8}{3} + \binom{8}{4} = \binom{\cdots}{4}$

  c Given that $\binom{9}{4} = 126$, write down the values of:

    i $\binom{9}{5}$
       ii $\binom{10}{5}$

2 Solve for n.

  a $\binom{n}{2} = 15$
       b $\binom{8}{n} = 70$
       c $\binom{n+2}{n} = 55$

  d $\binom{n+1}{2} - 2n = 9$
     e $\binom{n}{3} \div \binom{n-1}{2} = \frac{5}{3}$
     f $\binom{n+2}{n-1} + \binom{n+1}{n} = 14$

3 Show that:

  a $\binom{n}{4} + \binom{n}{5} = \binom{n+1}{5}$ where $n \geqslant 5$
     b $\binom{n+1}{4} - \binom{n}{4} = \binom{n}{3}$ where $n \geqslant 4$

  c $\binom{n}{5} - \binom{n-1}{4} = \binom{n-1}{5}$ where $n \geqslant 6$
   d $\binom{n}{n-r} = \binom{n}{r}$ where $1 \leqslant r \leqslant n$

4 Simplify.

a $\binom{n+1}{n-1}$ where $n \in \mathbb{N}$

b $\binom{n-2}{n-5}$ where $n \geqslant 5$

c $\binom{n}{3} - \binom{n}{2}$ where $n \geqslant 3$

d $\binom{n}{r-1} + \binom{n}{r}$ where $1 \leqslant r \leqslant n$

Exercise 1H The binomial theorem

1 Expand and simplify.

a $(3 + 2x)^4$

b $(y^2 - 2)^5$

c $(2m - 3n)^6$

d $\left(\dfrac{4}{x} + x^3\right)^5$

e $\left(2x - \dfrac{1}{x^2}\right)^6$

f $\left(\dfrac{x}{3} + \dfrac{3}{x}\right)^4$

g $\left(3x^3 - \dfrac{2}{x^3}\right)^5$

h $\left(\dfrac{5p^2}{3} - \dfrac{3}{p}\right)^4$

i $\left(\dfrac{1}{x} + 6x^4\right)^5$

j $(2 + x + x^2)^4$

| Hint | Treat this as $([2 + x] + x^2)^4$ |

2 Show that in the expansion of $\left(x - \dfrac{2}{x}\right)^{10}$ the term independent of x is -8064.

3 **i** Write down and simplify the general term in each expansion i.e. $\binom{n}{r}x^{n-r}y^r$

ii Use the general term to find the specific term given in [square brackets].

a $(2 + x^2)^{12}$ $[x^{18}]$

b $\left(3x + \dfrac{2}{x}\right)^{14}$ $[x^6]$

c $\left(\dfrac{2}{x} - 5x^2\right)^{10}$ $[x^5]$

d $\left(y^3 + \dfrac{2}{y^2}\right)^{11}$ $[y^8]$

e $\left(\dfrac{2}{x^3} - x^2\right)^{20}$ [term independent of x]

f $\left(\dfrac{3}{2x} + \dfrac{x^2}{3}\right)^{16}$ $[x^8]$

g $\left(p\sqrt{2} - \dfrac{1}{p}\right)^{17}$ $[p]$

h $\left(2x^6 - \dfrac{1}{3x^2}\right)^9$ $\left[\dfrac{1}{x^2}\right]$

Exercise 1I Approximations using the binomial theorem

1 For each of the following expansions
  i write down the first 4 terms in order of ascending powers of x
  ii estimate, to 3 significant figures, the answer to the given calculation by substituting a suitable value of x.

a $(1 + x)^{15}$, 1.01^{15}

b $(2 - x)^{12}$, 1.99^{12}

c $(2 + 3x)^8$, 2.18^8

d $(3 - 4x)^7$, 2.84^7

2 Use the binomial theorem to show that $1.2^5 = 2.48832$.

1 Obtain partial fractions for each expression.

a $\dfrac{1 - 3x}{(1 - x)^2}$

b $\dfrac{7x - 8}{(2x - 1)(x - 5)}$

c $\dfrac{1 + x^2}{(2 - x)(3 + x^2)}$

d $\dfrac{11x^2 - 59x + 74}{(1 + x)(3 - x)^2}$

e $\dfrac{7x - x^2 - 2}{2x + x^3}$

f $\dfrac{3 - 32x + 5x^2}{6x + 4x^2 - 2x^3}$

2 **a** Use algebraic division to show that $\dfrac{x + 1}{x - 1}$, $x \neq 1$, is equivalent to $1 + \dfrac{2}{x - 1}$

b The function, f, is defined on a suitable domain by $f(x) = \dfrac{x + 1}{x - 1}$

  i Find $f'(x)$.

  ii Deduce that the curve with equation $y = f(x)$ has no stationary points.

3 Write $\dfrac{2x^2 + 2x + 2}{x + 1}$, $x \neq -1$, in the form $kx + \dfrac{k}{x + 1}$ where k is a positive integer.

Hence find the coordinates of the stationary points on the curve $y = \dfrac{2x^2 + 2x + 2}{x + 1}$

4 Show that $\dfrac{2x^3 + 7x^2 + 4x - 3}{(x + 2)^2}$, $x \neq -2$, can be written in the form $ax + b + \dfrac{c}{(x + 2)^2}$

Hence obtain $\displaystyle\int \dfrac{2x^3 + 7x^2 + 4x - 3}{(x + 2)^2}\,dx$.

5 Let n be a whole number.

a Solve the equation $\dbinom{n}{1} + \dbinom{n}{2} = 28$

> **Hint**
>
> Remember that $\dbinom{n}{r - 1} + \dbinom{n}{r} = \dbinom{n + 1}{r}$

b Show that $\dbinom{n + 2}{3} - \dbinom{n}{3} = n^2$, for $n > 2$.

6 Let n be a whole number.

Express $\dbinom{n + 3}{n}^{-1}$ as a sum of partial fractions.

7 **a** Simplify $\ln 1 + \ln 2 + \ln 3 + \ldots + \ln(n - 1) + \ln n$.

b Hence use your calculator to find the smallest value of n such that
$\ln 1 + \ln 2 + \ln 3 + \ldots + \ln(n - 1) + \ln n > 200$.

8 Show that the general term in the expansion of $\left(\dfrac{1}{2x^4} + 8x^3\right)^{12}$ is given by:

$\dbinom{12}{r} \cdot 2^{4r - 12} \cdot x^{7r - 48}$

Hence find the coefficient of the term in x^{15}.

9 **a** Expand $\left(x - \dfrac{2}{x}\right)^4$, simplifying your answer.

b Hence evaluate $\displaystyle\int_1^2 \left(x - \dfrac{2}{x}\right)^4 dx$

10 Write $\ln\left(1 + 5x + 10x^2 + 10x^3 + 5x^4 + x^5\right)$ in the form $n \ln\left(m + x\right)$ and state the values of m and n.

11 **a** Write $1 - 8x + 24x^2 - 32x^3 + 16x^4$ in the form $\left(p - qx\right)^r$ where $p, q, r \in \mathbb{N}$.

b Hence obtain $\displaystyle\int \sin \sqrt[4]{1 - 8x + 24x^2 - 32x^3 + 16x^4}\ dx$

2 Differentiation

Exercise 2A Basic differentiation

1 Differentiate with respect to x.

a $y = 2x^6 + \cos 2x$

b $y = 2\sin x^2 + 4x$

c $f(x) = 7\cos \sqrt{x}$

d $y = (5 - 3x)^5 - \sin x$

e $f(x) = 5 + \sqrt{6x^2 - 2}$

f $f(x) = \cos^2 x - x^4$

g $y = \dfrac{3}{\sin 5x}$

h $f(x) = \dfrac{3}{\sqrt[4]{x + 1}} - 7x$

i $y = \cos(2 - x^3)^4$

j $y = 3\sin(\cos 4x)$

2 A curve has equation $y = 4\sin^2 3x$.

a Find $\dfrac{dy}{dx}$ in the form $p\sin qx$ where p and q are integers.

b Find the equation of the tangent to the curve at the point where $x = \dfrac{\pi}{12}$

Exercise 2B Differentiation of logarithmic and exponential functions

1 Find $\dfrac{dy}{dx}$ for each equation.

a $y = \ln(2 + 3x)$

b $y = 4\ln(\sin x)$

c $y = e^{4x-1}$

d $y = \cos e^{2x}$

e $y = (\ln x)^3$

f $y = (2x + 5)^3 - 2e^{-x}$

g $y = (7 - 2e^{3x})^6$

h $y = \dfrac{1}{\sqrt{1 - \ln x}}$

i $y = \sin^2(e^{2x})$

j $y = \dfrac{1}{x} - \cos(\ln 8x)$

k $y = \ln\sqrt{3 + x^2}$

l $y = \exp(\ln \sin x)$

m $y = \ln(xe^x)$

n $y = \ln\left(\dfrac{x - 1}{\ln x}\right)$

> **Hint** Remember the laws of logs.
> $\ln(AB) = \ln A + \ln B$
> $\ln\left(\dfrac{A}{B}\right) = \ln A - \ln B$
> $\ln(A^n) = n\ln A$

2 Show that the graph of the curve $y = e^{x^3 + 2x + 1}$ is always increasing.

Exercise 2C The product rule

1 Differentiate with respect to x.

a $y = x\cos x$

b $f(x) = x^5\sin 2x$

c $y = e^{3x}\cos 2x$

d $g(x) = (2 + x)^5(1 + 2x)^4$

e $y = 2x^6 e^{x^2}$

f $y = \sqrt{1 + 3x}\,\ln 4x$

g $f(x) = e^{-\cos x}\cos^3 2x$

h $g(x) = \ln(x\cos x + 1)$

i $y = \sqrt{x}\sin x$

j $f(x) = 2\sin(xe^{3x})$

k $y = \ln\left(\sqrt{x}\cos 2x\right)$

> **Hint** $\dfrac{d}{dx}(uv) = uv' + vu'$

2

a Given that $y = x(1 + x)^{10}$, show that $\frac{dy}{dx} = (11x + 1)(1 + x)^9$

b Given that $y = e^{\tan x} \cos^2 x$, show that $\frac{dy}{dx} = e^{\tan x}(1 - \sin 2x)$

3 A function, f, is defined by $f(x) = x^2 \ln\left(\frac{x}{2}\right)$, $x > 0$.

Find the rate of change of f when $x = 2$.

4 Part of the graph of the curve $y = 3xe^{2x}$ is shown in the diagram.

Find the coordinates of the minimum turning point on the graph.

Exercise 2D The quotient rule

1 Differentiate with respect to x.

a $y = \dfrac{2 + x}{x^2 + 1}$

b $f(x) = \dfrac{\sin x}{3x - 1}$

> **Hint** $\dfrac{d}{dx}\left(\dfrac{u}{v}\right) = \dfrac{vu' - uv'}{v^2}$

c $f(x) = \dfrac{\ln x}{2x}$

d $f(x) = \dfrac{e^{x+3}}{(x - 2)^3}$

e $y = \dfrac{\sin x}{\ln x}$

f $y = \dfrac{\sqrt{x^2 + 3}}{(2 - x)^2}$

g $f(x) = \dfrac{e^{\frac{x}{2}}}{\sin 3x}$

h $y = \sqrt{\dfrac{\cos x}{x^3}}$

> **Hint** Use laws of logs before differentiating.

i $y = \ln\left(\dfrac{1 + x}{x}\right)$

j $f(x) = \cos\left(\dfrac{1 + x}{1 - x}\right)$

2 A function is given by $f(x) = \dfrac{x - 1}{1 + \sqrt{x}}$, $x > 0$

Show that $f'(x) = \dfrac{1}{k\sqrt{x}}$ and state the value of the constant k.

3 Given that $y = \dfrac{\sin ax}{1 + \cos ax}$, where a is a constant, show that $\dfrac{dy}{dx} = \dfrac{a}{1 + \cos ax}$

Exercise 2E Higher derivatives

1 Find the second derivative, $f''(x)$.

a $f(x) = 6x^2 + 5x - 2$

b $f(x) = \sin(2x + 1)$

c $f(x) = 2\cos x^2$

d $f(x) = (1 - 4x)^5$

e $f(x) = \sqrt{2 + x}$

f $f(x) = 2e^{4x}$

g $f(x) = \ln(1 + 5x)$

h $f(x) = \dfrac{\ln x}{x}$

2 **a** Given that $y = (1 - 3x)^4$, find $\dfrac{d^3y}{dx^3}$

   b Find the fourth derivative of $f(x) = \ln(2x + 1)$.

   c **i** Find the first four derivatives of $y = e^{3x}$.

   ii Write down a formula for the nth derivative of $y = e^{3x}$.

3 Given that $y = (x - 1)^3(x - 4)$, show that $\dfrac{d^2y}{dx^2} = 6(x - 1)(2x - 5)$

4 Given that $y = \dfrac{\cos x}{1 - \sin x}$, show that $\dfrac{d^2y}{dx^2} = \dfrac{y}{1 - \sin x}$

5 The displacement, s metres, of a particle moving along a straight line after t seconds is given by $s = \dfrac{4}{3}t^3 - t^2 - 4t$

Find

   a the velocity of the particle after 2 seconds

   b the acceleration of the particle after 4 seconds.

6 A curve has equation $y = \dfrac{2 + x^2}{1 - x}$, $x \neq 1$

   a Find the coordinates of the stationary points on the graph of this curve.

   b Use $\dfrac{d^2y}{dx^2}$ to establish the nature of each stationary point.

Exercise 2F Differentiation of trigonometric functions

1 Differentiate with respect to x.

   a $f(x) = \sec \sqrt{x}$

   b $f(x) = \cot(2x^3)$

   c $f(x) = 2 + \tan\left(\dfrac{1}{x}\right)$

   d $f(x) = \dfrac{1}{2}\operatorname{cosec}(1 - x)$

   e $f(x) = \sqrt{\sec 4x}$

   f $f(x) = \dfrac{9}{1 + \tan x}$

   g $f(x) = 7\cot^2 x$

   h $g(x) = \sqrt{x}\tan x^2$

   i $y = (1 - x)^2 \sec x$

   j $f(x) = \dfrac{\tan 8x}{x^2}$

   k $f(x) = e^{x\tan x}$

   l $y = \left(\dfrac{\sec x}{x} + 1\right)^3$

2 Find the equation of the tangent to the curve $y = \operatorname{cosec} 2x$ at the point where $x = \dfrac{\pi}{8}$

3 Given that $f(x) = \sec 3x$, show that $f''(x) = 9\sec 3x(2\sec^2 3x - 1)$.

4 Given that $y = \tan x - x$, show that $\dfrac{d^2y}{dx^2} = 2\tan x(\tan^2 x + 1)$.

Exercise 2G Differentiation of inverse trigonometric functions

1 Differentiate with respect to x, simplifying your answer as much as possible.

   a $f(x) = \tan^{-1}(6x)$

   b $f(x) = \sin^{-1}(3x)$

   c $f(x) = 5\cos^{-1}(x^3)$

   d $g(x) = 9 + \sin^{-1}(1 - x)$

   e $h(x) = (\tan^{-1}x)^5$

   f $f(x) = \cos 2x + \cos^{-1} 2x$

   g $f(x) = \sqrt{\sin^{-1}x^2}$

   h $g(x) = e^{2\tan^{-1}x}$

   i $f(x) = \cos^{-1}\sqrt{\ln x}$

j $f(x) = \tan^{-1}(e^{3x}) + \dfrac{5}{x}$ **k** $y = 3x\tan^{-1}x$ **l** $f(x) = \dfrac{\sin^{-1}x}{x^3}$

m $f(x) = x^2(2 + \cos^{-1}x)$ **n** $g(x) = \dfrac{\cos^{-1}x}{e^{2x}}$ **o** $y = (2 + 5x)\sin^{-1}\sqrt{x}$

p $f(x) = \dfrac{\tan^{-1}2x}{\ln x}$ **q** $y = \dfrac{\cos^{-1}7x}{2 + e^x}$ **r** $y = \tan^{-1}\left(\dfrac{x}{1 + x}\right)$

s $f(x) = (x\sin^{-1}x)^2$ **t** $y = 8\tan^{-1}(xe^x)$

 2 Given that $f(x) = 3\sin^{-1}2x$, find $f''(x)$.

 3 The displacement, x metres, of a particle moving in a straight line after t seconds, is governed by the equation $x = \tan^{-1}t^2$, $t \geqslant 0$.

    a Find the velocity of the particle after two seconds.

    b Find a formula for the acceleration of the particle in terms of t.

    c Calculate the maximum speed attained by the particle in ms^{-1} correct to 3 significant figures.

Exercise 2H Implicit differentiation (first derivative)

Example 2.1

Given that $x^2 + y^3 - xy = 3$, find $\dfrac{dy}{dx}$

$2x + 3y^2\dfrac{dy}{dx} - \left(x\dfrac{dy}{dx} + y\right) = 0$ ———— Differentiate with respect to x. Use the product rule to differentiate the third term.

$\dfrac{dy}{dx}(3y^2 - x) = y - 2x$ ———— Collect the $\dfrac{dy}{dx}$ terms on the LHS and move the other terms to the RHS.

Take $\dfrac{dy}{dx}$ out as a common factor on the LHS.

$\dfrac{dy}{dx} = \dfrac{y - 2x}{3y^2 - x}$ ———— Divide both sides by $(3y^2 - x)$ to find an expression for $\dfrac{dy}{dx}$.

1 Find $\dfrac{dy}{dx}$ for the curves with these equations.

    a $2x - 3y + y^2 = 9$ **b** $3x^3 - xy = 2y$ **c** $x^2 - y^2 = 4xy$

    d $x^4y^3 + 5y = 0$ **e** $x + y = \ln y$ **f** $\sin x + \cos y = 2xy$

    g $e^x - e^y = 1 + y^3$ **h** $\sec y - \dfrac{1}{y} = x^2y + 2x$ **i** $x^5 + y\sqrt{x} = y\ln y$

    j $\sin^{-1}y + \cos^{-1}x = \dfrac{y}{x}$

2 Find the equation of the tangent to the curve $5xy + 2x - y = 10$ at the point $(1, 2)$.

3 Find the gradient of the tangent to the curve $4x + \ln y = xy^2$ at the point where its graph intersects the y-axis.

4   Find the equation of the tangent to the curve $x^3y + 5y^2 + 34 = 0$ at the point where $y = 2$.

5   A curve is given by $2y^2 - 2xy - 4y + x^2 = 0$.
    Find the x-coordinate of each point at which the curve has a horizontal tangent.

6   Show that the curve with equation $x^2 + 2y - xy = 4x$ has no stationary points.

7   Given that $\sqrt{x + y} = y - x$, show that $\dfrac{dy}{dx} = \dfrac{2y - 2x + 1}{2y - 2x - 1}$

8   Given that $(x + y)^3 = 3xy$, show that $\dfrac{dy}{dx} = \dfrac{y(y - 2x)}{x(2y - x)}$

9   The path of a particle, moving in a plane relative to a fixed origin, is given by the equation
    $$x^2y - 3y = 2x - 4$$
    Determine the distance between the particle and the origin at each of the points where $\dfrac{dy}{dx} = 0$.

10 a Given that $y = \sec^{-1}x$, show that $\dfrac{dy}{dx} = \dfrac{1}{x\sqrt{x^2 - 1}}$

    b Find the derivative of $\cot^{-1}x$.

Exercise 2I Implicit differentiation (second derivative)

1   Find $\dfrac{dy}{dx}$ and $\dfrac{d^2y}{dx^2}$ for the curves with these equations.

    a $x^2 + y^2 - 4x + 2y = 16$ b $5xy + 2y^2 = 10$ c $xy - 4y^3 = 1$

    d $\dfrac{x^3 + y^3}{y} = 12$ e $xy - \sqrt{y} = 4$ f $x + y = e^y$

    g $2x + y + \tan^{-1}y = 0$ h $y\ln y = 5x^2$

2   a Find the coordinates of the stationary point on the curve
          $$x^2 + 2xy + y^3 = 0 , y > 0$$
    b Determine the nature of the stationary point.

Exercise 2J Logarithmic differentiation

1   Use logarithmic differentiation to find $\dfrac{dy}{dx}$ in terms of x.

    a $y = 8^x$ b $y = 4^{\tan x}$ c $y = 2^{e^x}$

    d $y = 6^{\sec x + 1}$ e $y = x^{x^2 - 2}$ f $y = x^{\sin^{-1}x}$

    g $y = (\cos x)^{2x}$ h $y = (\ln x)^{x - 1}$ i $y = x^3 e^{4x}\cot x$

    j $y = \dfrac{5x^2\sin 3x}{(x + 1)\ln x}$

    Hint   Remember that if c is a constant, then $\ln c$ is a constant.

2 For the curve with equation $y = (x + 3)^{x-2}$

  a find the coordinates of the point, P, where the graph crosses the y-axis

  b find the value of $\dfrac{dy}{dx}$ at P, correct to 3 significant figures.

3 Given that $y = (x + 1)^2(x + 2)^{-4}$, use logarithmic differentiation to show that $\dfrac{dy}{dx}$ can be written in the form

$$\left(\frac{a}{x + 1} + \frac{b}{x + 2}\right) y$$

and state the values of the constants a and b.

4 The diagram shows part of the graph of the curve with equation $y = x^x$, $x > 0$.

Point A is the minimum turning point on the graph.

Find the x-coordinate of A.

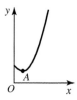

5 The position of a particle moving along a straight line relative to the origin, O, at time t is given by

$$x = (\sin 4t)^{\tan 2t} \text{ where } 0 < t < \frac{\pi}{4}$$

Show that the particle is at rest when $t = \dfrac{\pi}{8}$

Exercise 2K Parametric differentiation

1 Find $\dfrac{dy}{dx}$ for the curves with these parametric equations.

  a $x = 2t^2 - 1, \quad y = 3 - 4t$

  b $x = 6t^5 + 4t, \quad y = t^3 - \dfrac{1}{t^2}$

  c $x = 2\cos\theta, \quad y = 4\sin\theta$

  d $x = \sqrt{t + 2}, \quad y = 5t^2 - 4t - 2$

  e $x = \ln(1 + t), \quad y = 8\sqrt{t}$

  f $x = \sec 3\theta, \quad y = 2\tan^2 3\theta$

  g $x = \sin^{-1} t, \quad y = 2\cos^{-1}(2t)$

  h $x = \dfrac{2}{t}, \quad y = 1 + e^{-t}$

  i $x = \cot 2\theta, \quad y = 2 + 5\operatorname{cosec} 2\theta$

  j $x = \cos\theta, \quad y = \theta\sin\theta$

2 Find $\dfrac{dy}{dx}$ and $\dfrac{d^2y}{dx^2}$ for the curves with these parametric equations.

  a $x = 2 + t^2, \quad y = t^3 - 2t$

  b $x = \dfrac{3}{t} + t, \quad y = \dfrac{2}{t^4} + 4$

  c $x = \ln t + \dfrac{1}{2t}, \quad y = 6t^3 - 7t^2$

  d $x = 1 + e^{2t}, \quad y = t(3t - 1)$

  e $x = \sin\theta, \quad y = \theta\cos\theta$

  f $x = \sqrt{\tan 2\theta}, \quad y = 2\sec 2\theta$

  g $x = \sin^{-1}(1 - t), \quad y = \cos^{-1}(1 - t)$

  h $x = (\ln t)^2, \quad y = 2\ln t$

3 A curve is defined by the equations

$$x = 5\cos\theta \text{ and } y = 5\sin\theta \text{ for } 0 \le \theta < 2\pi$$

a Show that $\dfrac{dy}{dx} = -\cot\theta$

b Find the equation of the tangent to the curve at the point where $\theta = \dfrac{\pi}{4}$

4 A curve is defined by the equations

$$x = t^2 + 2t - 3 \text{ and } y = t^2 - 8t + 1$$

Find the coordinates of the stationary point on the curve and determine its nature.

5 A curve is given by the parametric equations

$$x = \sqrt{t^3 + 1} \text{ and } y = t(t^3 - 3) \text{ for } t \ge -1$$

Find the equation of the tangent to the curve at the point where $x = 3$.

6 Prove that the curve described by the equations

$$x = 2t^3 + 5 \text{ and } y = t^3 - 3t^2 + 6t - 1$$

has no stationary points.

7 The position of a particle moving in a plane after t seconds is given by the equations

$$x = t(t^2 + 2) \text{ and } y = 2\sqrt{7 + t^2}$$

where x and y are the horizontal and vertical displacements respectively.

Find the instantaneous speed of the particle after 4 seconds, correct to 3 significant figures.

8 Given that $x = 3\cos t$ and $y = 2\sin t$, show that $\dfrac{d^2y}{dx^2} = -\dfrac{2}{9}\operatorname{cosec}^3 t$

9 Given that $x = \cot^3 t$ and $y = 2\operatorname{cosec}^2 t$, show that $\dfrac{d^2y}{dx^2} = -\dfrac{4}{9}\tan^4 t$

10 The path of a robot roaming the floor of a large room relative to a fixed origin, O, is modelled by the equations

$$x = t\cos t \text{ and } y = t(1 + t)$$

where t represents time in seconds.

The graph shows part of the robot's journey.

Both axes are scaled in metres.

Point P indicates one of the positions where the robot's path crosses the y-axis.

Calculate the speed of the robot at P.

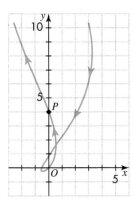

Example 2.2

A rectangle has length L cm and breadth B cm.

The length of the rectangle increases at a rate of $0.06\,\mathrm{cm\,s^{-1}}$.

The breadth of the rectangle decreases at a rate of $0.02\,\mathrm{cm\,s^{-1}}$.

Find the rate of change of the area, A, of the rectangle when $L = 4.5$ and $B = 2.9$.

$A = LB$ ————————————————————— Begin with the formula for the area of the rectangle.

$\dfrac{dA}{dt} = L\dfrac{dB}{dt} + B\dfrac{dL}{dt}$ ————— Differentiate implicitly with respect to t. The product rule has been used here.

$\dfrac{dA}{dt} = 4.5 \times (-0.02) + 2.9 \times 0.06 = 0.084\,\mathrm{cm^2\,s^{-1}}.$ ———— Substitute the relevant values of L, B, $\dfrac{dL}{dt}$ and $\dfrac{dB}{dt}$ and evaluate. $\dfrac{dB}{dt}$ is negative because B is decreasing with time.

1 A circle has area A and circumference C.

Find an expression for $\dfrac{dA}{dC}$ in terms of C.

2 A metal cube of length x grows in size (but remains the same shape) when heated.

The volume of the cube increases at constant rate of $0.006\,\mathrm{cm^3\,s^{-1}}$.

Find the rate of change of the length of the cube when its volume is $8\,\mathrm{cm^3}$.

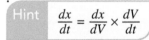 Hint $\dfrac{dx}{dt} = \dfrac{dx}{dV} \times \dfrac{dV}{dt}$

3 A right-angled triangle has base length x cm, height y cm and hypotenuse of length z cm.

The base length of the triangle increases at a constant rate of $2\,\mathrm{cm\,s^{-1}}$ and the height decreases such that the area of the triangle is always equal to $30\,\mathrm{cm^2}$.

Find the rate of change of the hypotenuse when $x = 12$.

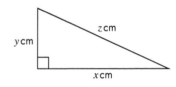

4 Air escapes from a spherical balloon at a rate of $3\,\mathrm{cm^3}$ per minute.

Determine how quickly the surface area of the balloon is changing when the radius is $8\,\mathrm{cm}$.

Hint A sphere of radius r has volume $V = \dfrac{4}{3}\pi r^3$, and surface area $S = 4\pi r^2$

5 A cylinder with radius r and height h is being flattened but its volume remains constant.

At the particular moment when the radius is $6\,\mathrm{cm}$, the height is $8\,\mathrm{cm}$ and the height decreases at $0.3\,\mathrm{cm\,s^{-1}}$.

At that moment, what is the rate of change of the radius?

6 A paper cup in the shape of a cone has diameter $6\,\mathrm{cm}$ and height $10\,\mathrm{cm}$.

Water leaks out from the bottom of the cup at a rate of $0.5\,\mathrm{cm^3\,s^{-1}}$.

How quickly does the water level drop when the depth of the water is $4\,\mathrm{cm}$?

Hint Volume of a cone with base radius r and height h is $V = \dfrac{1}{3}\pi r^2 h$

Chapter review

1 Differentiate each function with respect to x.

a $y = 8x^3 + \sqrt{x} - 5$

b $y = \sin 4x + 2\cos 6x$

c $y = 7\ln x + \dfrac{1}{x}$

d $f(x) = 9e^{10x}$

e $y = 6\tan(\ln x)$

f $f(x) = 4x^3 \cos x$

g $y = \sec(4e^{2x})$

h $f(x) = \sin^{-1}(x^5)$

i $y = 6^{2x+1}$

j $f(x) = \dfrac{5-x}{1+3x}$

k $y = 4\cot\sqrt{x-1}$

l $y = \sqrt[3]{\operatorname{cosec} 3x}$

m $f(x) = e^{3x}\cos^{-1}\sqrt{x}$

n $y = \dfrac{e^{\sin x}}{(1+2x)^2}$

o $f(x) = \tan^{-1}\left(\dfrac{x}{3}\right)$

p $y = \dfrac{2}{(1+\ln x)^4}$

q $f(x) = (x+2)^{\sec 2x}$

r $y = \left(\sin^{-1}\sqrt{1-x}\right)^2$

s $f(x) = \cot(xe^{3x})$

t $f(x) = 5\ln\left(\dfrac{2+x}{x^3}\right)$

u $y = \sqrt{\cos^3(x^4+2)}$

2 Find $f''(x)$ for each function $f(x)$.

a $f(x) = 2\sin^{-1} 3x$

b $f(x) = \operatorname{cosec} 5x$

c $f(x) = \dfrac{3x+2}{x^2+4}$

d $f(x) = 12\ln(2x^2+1)$

3 A circle has equation $x^2 + y^2 + 6x - 12y + 20 = 0$

a Find $\dfrac{dy}{dx}$

b Hence find the equation of the tangent to the circle at the point $(1, 3)$.

4 A curve has equation $5x + 4y - 2xy = 6$

Find $\dfrac{dy}{dx}$ and $\dfrac{d^2y}{dx^2}$ in terms of x and y.

5 The position of a particle in a plane with respect to a fixed origin, O, is given by the equations

$$x = t(t-2) \text{ and } y = \sqrt{e^t}$$

where t represent time in seconds.

Given that all units are in metres, find the instantaneous speed of the particle after 3 seconds, correct to 3 significant figures.

6 A curve has parametric equations

$$x = 5t + \sqrt{t} \text{ and } y = t^2 - 8t - 2 \text{ where } t > 0.$$

a Find $\dfrac{dy}{dx}$ and $\dfrac{d^2y}{dx^2}$ in terms of t.

b Find the coordinates of the stationary point on the curve and determine its nature.

7 The area, A, of an ellipse is given by the formula

$$A = \pi R r$$

where R is the major radius and r is the minor radius, as indicated in the diagram.

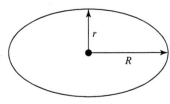

Initially, the major radius is 12 cm and the minor radius is 5 cm but changes as follows:

- the major radius increases at a rate of $0.052\,\text{cm}\,\text{s}^{-1}$

- the minor radius increases at a rate of $0.036\,\text{cm}\,\text{s}^{-1}$.

Find:

a the initial area of the ellipse

b the area after 1 minute

c the rate of increase of the area after 1 minute.

8 The volume of a sphere is given by $V = \frac{4}{3}\pi r^3$ and its surface area by $A = 4\pi r^2$.

The volume of the sphere is increasing at a steady rate of $5\,\text{cm}^3\,\text{s}^{-1}$.

a Show that $\dfrac{dr}{dt} = \dfrac{5}{A}$.

b Calculate the rate of increase of the surface area when the radius is 4 cm.

9 The position (x, y) of a particle moving through a plane relative to a fixed origin, O, is given by the equations

$$x = t^3 - 2t \text{ and } y = 3t^2$$

where t represents time in seconds.

a Find the instantaneous speed of the particle after 3 seconds.

b Find the absolute value of the acceleration of the particle after 4 seconds.

10 The diagram shows the graphs of $y = \sec x$ and $y = \sin^2 x$ for $0 \leqslant x \leqslant \dfrac{\pi}{3}$

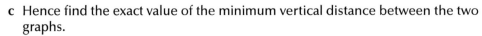

Let $g(x)$ denote the length of the vertical distance between the two graphs.

a Show that:

   i $g(x)$ can be written in the form
$$g(x) = \frac{\cos^3 x - \cos x + 1}{\cos x}$$

   ii $g(x)$ attains its minimum value when $x = \cos^{-1}\left(\dfrac{1}{\sqrt[3]{2}}\right)$

c Hence find the exact value of the minimum vertical distance between the two graphs.

3 Integration

Exercise 3A Basic integration

1 Find these integrals.

a $\int (6x^2 + 5x - 2)dx$

b $\int \left(8\sqrt{x} - \cos 2x\right)dx$

c $\int \dfrac{7}{(2x + 9)^2}\, dx$

d $\int \cos(\pi + 4x)dx$

e $\int \dfrac{1}{\sqrt[3]{5x + 2}}\, dx$

f $\int 9\sin(1 - 3x)dx$

g $\int \left(\sqrt[5]{x^2} + \sin 8x\right)dx$

h $\int \dfrac{(3x + 5)^2}{\sqrt{x}}\, dx$

2 Evaluate these integrals.

a $\int_0^{\frac{\pi}{8}} 2\sin 4x\, dx$

b $\int_1^2 (3 - 2x)^4\, dx$

c $\int_1^3 \dfrac{4x^3 + 3x^2 - 1}{x^2}\, dx$

d $\int_{\frac{1}{4}}^4 \sqrt{x}\left(1 - \dfrac{1}{\sqrt{x}}\right) dx$

e $\int_{-1}^1 (2 + x^3)^2\, dx$

f $\int_{\frac{2}{5}}^1 \left(3 - \sqrt{6 - 5x}\right) dx$

g $\int_0^{\pi} 4\cos\left(\dfrac{x + 2\pi}{3}\right) dx$

h $\int_1^{16} \sqrt[4]{\dfrac{8}{x}}\, dx$

Exercise 3B Integration using trigonometric identities

1 Find these integrals.

a $\int 6\sin x \cos x\, dx$

b $\int (\sin x + \cos x)(\sin x - \cos x)\, dx$

c $\int 2\sin^2 x\, dx$

d $\int (3 - 2\cos^2 x)\, dx$

e $\int \tan 3x \cos 3x\, dx$

f $\int \dfrac{4\sin 6x}{\sin 3x}\, dx$

g $\int (1 - 2\sin^2 x)^2\, dx$

h $\int (\sin^4 x - \cos^4 x)\, dx$

> **Hint** Remember these trigonometric identities.
>
> $\dfrac{\sin A}{\cos A} \equiv \tan A$ $\qquad \sin^2 A + \cos^2 A \equiv 1 \qquad \sin 2A \equiv 2\sin A \cos A$
>
> $\cos 2A \equiv \cos^2 A - \sin^2 A \quad \cos 2A \equiv 2\cos^2 A - 1 \quad \cos 2A \equiv 1 - 2\sin^2 A$
>
> $\sin^2 A \equiv \dfrac{1}{2}(1 - \cos 2A)$ (Useful for integrating $\sin^2 x$)
>
> $\cos^2 A \equiv \dfrac{1}{2}(1 + \cos 2A)$ (Useful for integrating $\cos^2 x$)

2 Evaluate these integrals.

a $\int_0^{\frac{\pi}{2}}(\cos 2x + \sin 2x)^2\,dx$ **b** $\int_{\frac{\pi}{4}}^{\pi}\cos^2 3x\,dx$

c $\int_{\pi}^{2\pi}\sqrt{1+\cos 2x}\,dx$ **d** $\int_1^3\sqrt{\cos 4x + 2\sin^2 2x}\,dx$

Exercise 3C Integration of exponential and reciprocal linear functions

1 Find these integrals.

a $\int e^{4x}\,dx$ **b** $\int \frac{8}{x}\,dx$

c $\int 4e^{3-x}\,dx$ **d** $\int\left(\sin 2x - \frac{3}{x-1}\right)dx$

e $\int\left(\frac{e^{3x}-1}{e^x}\right)dx$ **f** $\int\left(\frac{5}{2x-1} - \cos 3x\right)dx$

g $\int\left(2e^{\frac{x}{2}} + 4\sqrt{x}\right)dx$ **h** $\int\left(e^{\ln x} + e^{-\ln x}\right)dx$

2 Evaluate these integrals.

a $\int_1^3 \frac{dx}{1+2x}$ **b** $\int_0^1(e^{2x}+1)\,dx$

c $\int_0^1(e^x+1)^2\,dx$ **d** $\int_2^4 \frac{3x^3+6x^2-2x+5}{x}\,dx$

Exercise 3D Integration of trigonometric functions using anti-differentiation

1 Find these integrals.

a $\int(6x^2 + \sec^2 x)\,dx$ **b** $\int \text{cosec}^2\,2x\,dx$ **c** $\int \sec x(\sec x + \tan x)\,dx$

d $\int 4\tan^2 x\,dx$ **e** $\int \frac{\sin 2x}{\cos^2 2x}\,dx$ **f** $\int \frac{dx}{(1-2\sin^2 3x)^2}$

> **Hint** Learn these useful trigonometric identities.
>
> $\frac{\cos A}{\sin A} \equiv \cot A$ $\quad 1+\tan^2 A \equiv \sec^2 A$ $\quad 1+\cot^2 A \equiv \text{cosec}^2 A$

2 Evaluate these integrals.

a $\int_{\frac{\pi}{12}}^{\frac{\pi}{8}} \text{cosec}\,4x\cot 4x\,dx$ **b** $\int_0^{\frac{\pi}{18}}(1-\sec 3x)(1+\sec 3x)\,dx$

c $\int_{\frac{\pi}{3}}^{\frac{\pi}{2}} \frac{\cos\left(\frac{x}{2}\right)}{\sin^2\left(\frac{x}{2}\right)}\,dx$ **d** $\int_{\frac{\pi}{6}}^{\frac{\pi}{3}} \frac{dx}{\text{cosec}^2 x - 1}$

3 **a** Show that $1+\cot^2 A \equiv \text{cosec}^2 A$.

b Hence obtain $\int \cot^2 x\,dx$.

Exercise 3E Integration resulting in inverse trigonometric functions

1 Find these integrals.

a $\int \dfrac{dx}{9 + x^2}$　　　　　　**b** $\int \dfrac{dx}{\sqrt{4 - x^2}}$　　　　　　**c** $\int \dfrac{3dx}{\sqrt{16 - x^2}}$

d $\int \dfrac{dx}{\sqrt{7 - x^2}}$　　　　　　**e** $\int \dfrac{dx}{8 + 2x^2}$　　　　　　**f** $\int \dfrac{dx}{\sqrt{8 - 4x^2}}$

g $\int \dfrac{2dx}{3x^2 + 4}$　　　　　　**h** $\int \dfrac{dx}{\sqrt{16 - 9x^2}}$　　　　　　**i** $\int \dfrac{dx}{4x^2 + 9}$

j $\int \dfrac{2x - 7}{9 + x^2} dx$

2 Evaluate these integrals.

a $\displaystyle\int_{5}^{5\sqrt{3}} \dfrac{4dx}{x^2 + 25}$　　　　**b** $\displaystyle\int_{0}^{5} \dfrac{dx}{\sqrt{25 - x^2}}$　　　　**c** $\displaystyle\int_{0}^{3} \dfrac{dx}{36 + 4x^2}$

d $\displaystyle\int_{0}^{\frac{1}{\sqrt{5}}} \dfrac{dx}{\sqrt{4 - 5x^2}}$　　**e** $\displaystyle\int_{\frac{5}{6}}^{\frac{5}{3}} \sqrt{\dfrac{4}{(5 - 3x)(5 + 3x)}}\, dx$　　**f** $\displaystyle\int_{-\sqrt{6}}^{-\sqrt{2}} \dfrac{2 - x^2}{4 - x^4}\, dx$

3　**a** Write $x^2 - 8x + 25$ in the form $(x - p)^2 + q$.

　　b Hence obtain $\int \dfrac{dx}{x^2 - 8x + 25}$

4　**a** Write $6x - x^2 - 5$ in the form $m - (x - n)^2$.

　　b Hence evaluate $\displaystyle\int_{2}^{4} \dfrac{dx}{\sqrt{6x - x^2 - 5}}$

Exercise 3F Integration of rational functions using partial fractions

1　**a** Write $\dfrac{x - 1}{(x + 2)(x + 1)}$ in terms of partial fractions.

　　b Hence obtain $\int \dfrac{x - 1}{(x + 2)(x + 1)} dx$

2　**a** Write $\dfrac{6x + 1}{(2x - 1)^2}$ as a sum of partial fractions.

　　b Hence find the exact value of $\displaystyle\int_{1}^{2} \dfrac{6x + 1}{(2x - 1)^2} dx$

3　**a** Obtain partial fractions for $\dfrac{3x^2 - x + 5}{(2 - x)(1 + x^2)}$

　　b Hence find $\int \dfrac{3x^2 - x + 5}{(2 - x)(1 + x^2)} dx$

4　**a** Write $\dfrac{2x^3 + 11x^2 + 10x - 9}{x(x + 3)^2}$ as a quotient and a sum of partial fractions.

　　b Hence show that $\displaystyle\int_{-2}^{-1} \dfrac{2x^3 + 11x^2 + 10x - 9}{x(x + 3)^2} dx = 1 + \ln 2$

5 Find these integrals.

a $\displaystyle\int \frac{3x^2 + 13x + 2}{(2x + 1)(x + 2)(x - 2)} dx$

b $\displaystyle\int \frac{7x^2 - 5x + 1}{x^2(x - 1)} dx$

c $\displaystyle\int \frac{3x^3 - 3x^2 + 3x - 2}{x^3 + x} dx$

d $\displaystyle\int \frac{x^2(x + 1)}{x^2 + 4} dx$

6 Evaluate $\displaystyle\int_0^{\sqrt{2}} \frac{2x^4 + 3x^3 + 7x^2 + 5x - 2}{(x + 2)(x^2 + 2)} dx$ correct to 3 significant figures.

Exercise 3G Indefinite integration using a given substitution

1 Obtain the following integrals using the given substitution.

a $\displaystyle\int 2x\cos(x^2 - 1)dx$ [let $u = x^2 - 1$]

b $\displaystyle\int \frac{1 + x}{3 + 2x + x^2} dx$ [let $u = 3 + 2x + x^2$]

c $\displaystyle\int e^x \sec e^x \tan e^x \, dx$ [let $u = e^x$]

d $\displaystyle\int \frac{x}{\sqrt{x + 3}} dx$ [let $u = x + 3$]

e $\displaystyle\int \frac{dx}{\sin x \cos x}$ [let $u = \tan x$]

f $\displaystyle\int \sec x \, dx$ [let $u = \sec x + \tan x$]

g $\displaystyle\int \frac{2x}{\sqrt{1 - x^4}} dx$ [let $x = \sqrt{\cos u}$]

h $\displaystyle\int \frac{1}{13 + 6x + x^2} dx$ [let $u = x + 3$]

2 Obtain $\displaystyle\int x^3(x^2 - 8)^{\frac{1}{3}} dx$ by means of the substitution $u = x^2 - 8$.

3 Use the substitution $x = 2\sin\theta$ to show that

$$\int \sqrt{4 - x^2} \, dx = 2\sin^{-1}\left(\frac{x}{2}\right) + \frac{1}{2}x\sqrt{4 - x^2} + c$$

Exercise 3H Indefinite integration by substitution or anti-differentiation

 1 Obtain each integral by making a suitable substitution or recognising an anti-derivative.

a $\displaystyle\int \frac{3x^2 + 1}{x^3 + x - 2}\,dx$ **b** $\displaystyle\int \frac{x - 3}{x^2 - 6x - 4}\,dx$ **c** $\displaystyle\int \tan 2x\,dx$

d $\displaystyle\int \frac{2x + 7}{(x + 3)^2}\,dx$ **e** $\displaystyle\int \cot 5x\,dx$ **f** $\displaystyle\int \frac{dx}{x \ln x}$

> **Hint** $\displaystyle\int \frac{f'(x)}{f(x)}\,dx = \ln|f(x)| + c$

 2 Obtain these integrals.

a $\displaystyle\int 2xe^{x^2}\,dx$ **b** $\displaystyle\int 3e^{\tan x} \sec^2 x\,dx$ **c** $\displaystyle\int x^2 \cos x^3\,dx$

d $\displaystyle\int \frac{\cos^{-1} x}{\sqrt{1 - x^2}}\,dx$ **e** $\displaystyle\int e^{\sin 2x} \cos 2x\,dx$ **f** $\displaystyle\int \left(x^3 - \frac{1}{x}\right)^3 \left(3x^2 + \frac{1}{x^2}\right)dx$

3 Use a suitable substitution to obtain $\displaystyle\int \frac{x}{\sqrt{1 - 9x^4}}\,dx$

4 Find $\displaystyle\int \left(\frac{\cos x}{x} - \ln x \sin x\right)dx$

Exercise 3I Evaluating definite integrals by substitution

> ### Example 3.1
> Use the substitution $u = x^2 + 1$ to evaluate $\displaystyle\int_0^1 \frac{3x(x^2 + 2)}{\sqrt{x^2 + 1}}\,dx$

$\dfrac{du}{dx} = 2x \Leftrightarrow dx = \dfrac{du}{2x}$ •——— Differentiate the substitution equation and make dx the subject.

Limits: $x = 1 \Rightarrow u = 1^2 + 1 = 2$ and $x = 0 \Rightarrow u = 0^2 + 1 = 1$ •——— Find the new limits.

Integral becomes:

$\displaystyle\int_1^2 \frac{3x(u + 1)}{\sqrt{u}} \frac{du}{2x} = \frac{3}{2}\int_1^2 \frac{(u + 1)}{\sqrt{u}}\,du = \frac{3}{2}\int_1^2 \left(\sqrt{u} + \frac{1}{\sqrt{u}}\right)du$ •——— Replace $x^2 + 1$ with u and dx with $\dfrac{du}{2x}$ and simplify so that the integral is in terms of u only.

$\displaystyle = \frac{3}{2}\left[\frac{2}{3}\sqrt{u^3} + 2\sqrt{u}\right]_1^2$

$\displaystyle = \frac{3}{2}\left\{\left[\frac{2}{3}\sqrt{8} + 2\sqrt{2}\right] - \left[\frac{2}{3} + 2\right]\right\}$

$\displaystyle = \frac{3}{2}\left\{\left[\frac{4\sqrt{2}}{3} + 2\sqrt{2}\right] - \left[\frac{8}{3}\right]\right\} = \frac{3}{2}\left\{\frac{10\sqrt{2} - 8}{3}\right\} = 5\sqrt{2} - 4$ •——— Evaluate integral

1 Evaluate each of the following definite integrals using the substitution given.

a $\int_0^{\sqrt{5}} \frac{6x}{\sqrt{4+x^2}}\,dx$ [let $u = 4 + x^2$]   **b** $\int_1^e \frac{1}{x(1+\ln x)^2}\,dx$ [let $u = 1 + \ln x$]

c $\int_{-7}^0 \frac{x^2+5x-7}{\sqrt[3]{1-x}}\,dx$ [let $u = 1 - x$]   **d** $\int_0^{\frac{\pi}{4}} e^{\sin^2 x}\sin x \cos x\,dx$ [let $u = \sin^2 x$]

e $\int_0^{\frac{\pi}{3}} \sin^3 x\,dx$ [let $u = \cos x$]   **f** $\int_{\frac{\pi}{12}}^{\frac{\pi}{4}} \cot 2x\,dx$ [let $u = \sin 2x$]

g $\int_{-\sqrt{3}}^0 \sqrt{4-x^2}\,dx$ [let $x = 2\sin\theta$]   **h** $\int_{\frac{2}{\sqrt{3}}}^2 \frac{1}{x\sqrt{x^2-1}}\,dx$ [let $x = \sec u$]

i $\int_0^{\sqrt{2}} \frac{8x}{4+x^4}\,dx$ [let $x^2 = 2\tan\theta$]   **j** $\int_{\frac{\pi}{3}}^{\frac{\pi}{2}} \frac{x\cos x - \sin x}{x^2}\,dx$ [let $xu = \sin x$]

> **Hint** Differentiate the substitution implicitly i.e. $2x\frac{dx}{d\theta} = 2\sec^2\theta$

2 Use a suitable substitution to evaluate $\int_{\frac{\pi^2}{4}}^{\pi^2} \frac{\sin\sqrt{x}}{2\sqrt{x}}\,dx$

3 Use the substitution $u = \cos x$ to show that the exact value of $\int_0^{\frac{\pi}{6}} \sin^3 x \cos^5 x\,dx$

is $\frac{67}{6144}$.

Exercise 3J Integration of higher powers of trigonometric functions

1 Use the substitution $u = \cos 2x$ to obtain $\int \sin^3 2x\,dx$

2 Evaluate $\int_0^{\frac{\pi}{4}} \cos^4\left(\frac{x}{2}\right)dx$ correct to 3 significant figures.

> **Hint** For even powers of sines or cosines use $\sin^2 A = \frac{1}{2}(1 - \cos 2A)$
>
> or $\cos^2 A = \frac{1}{2}(1 + \cos 2A)$

3 Use a suitable substitution to find $\int \cos^5\theta\,d\theta$

4 **a** Use the substitution $u = \tan x$ to obtain $\int \sec^4 x\,dx$

b Hence find the exact value of $\int_0^{\frac{\pi}{3}} \tan^4 x\,dx$

5 **a** Show that $\operatorname{cosec}^2 A - \cot^2 A \equiv 1$

b Use the substitution $x = \operatorname{cosec}\theta$ to find $\int \cot^3\theta\,d\theta$

6 **a** Show that $\int \cos^3 2x\, dx = \frac{1}{2}\sin 2x - \frac{1}{6}\sin^3 2x + c$

b Hence evaluate $\int_0^{\frac{\pi}{8}} \sin^6 x\, dx$ correct to 4 decimal places.

Exercise 3K Integration by parts (one application)

1 Find these integrals.

a $\int x \cos x\, dx$

b $\int (1+x)\sin 2x\, dx$

c $\int \sqrt{x}\, \ln x\, dx$

d $\int 3x \sec^2 x\, dx$

e $\int (2x+3)e^{4x}\, dx$

f $\int (1-2x)\operatorname{cosec}^2 2x\, dx$

g $\int \ln 3x\, dx$

h $\int \sin^{-1} x\, dx$

> **Hint** When deciding which factor is to be u, use the order:
> **1** Logarithmic and inverse trigonometric expressions
> **2** Whole number powers of x
> **3** Trigonometric and exponential expressions

2 Evaluate these integrals.

a $\int_0^{\frac{\pi}{6}} 2x \sin 3x\, dx$

b $\int_2^3 (x-1)^3 \ln(x-1)\, dx$

c $\int_0^1 (5+2x)e^{-x}\, dx$

d $\int_2^4 \ln\sqrt{x}\, dx$

e $\int_{\frac{1}{2}}^1 \frac{\sqrt{1-x^2}}{x^2}\, dx$

f $\int_0^1 \tan^{-1} x\, dx$

3 **a** Given that $f(x) = \sqrt{\cos x}$, find $f'(x)$.

b i If, in general, $f(x) = \sqrt{g(x)}$, where $g(x) \geqslant 0$, show that

$$f'(x) = \frac{g'(x)}{k\sqrt{g(x)}}, \text{ stating the value of } k.$$

ii Hence, or otherwise, show that $\int \frac{x}{\sqrt{1-x^2}}\, dx = c - \sqrt{1-x^2}$

c Use integration by parts and the result of part **b** to obtain $\int \cos^{-1} x\, dx$

4 **a** Show that $\frac{d}{dx}(xe^{2x}) = e^{2x}(2x+1)$

b Hence find the exact value of $\int_0^{\frac{1}{2}} \frac{xe^{2x}}{(1+2x)^2}\, dx$

Exercise 3L Integration by parts (two applications)

Example 3.2

Use integration by parts to obtain $\int (x+1)^2 \cos 2x \, dx$

$u = (x+1)^2 \Rightarrow u' = 2(x+1)$ and $v' = \cos 2x \Rightarrow v = \frac{1}{2}\sin 2x$ — Select u and v' then find u' and v.

Integral becomes:

$\frac{1}{2}(x+1)^2 \sin 2x - \int (x+1)\sin 2x \, dx$ — Use integration by parts: $\int uv' = uv - \int vu'$

$= \frac{1}{2}(x+1)^2 \sin 2x - \left(-\frac{1}{2}(x+1)\cos 2x + \frac{1}{2}\int \cos 2x \, dx\right)$ — Use integration by parts again with $u = x+1$ and $v' = \sin 2x$.

$= \frac{1}{2}(x+1)^2 \sin 2x + \frac{1}{2}(x+1)\cos 2x - \frac{1}{4}\sin 2x + c$ — Perform the final integration and simplify. Remember to add the constant of integration.

1 Find these integrals.

a $\int x^2 \sin x \, dx$

b $\int 4x^2 e^{2x} \, dx$

c $\int (x-1)^2 \cos 3x \, dx$

d $\int (x^2 + 2x + 2)(2x+3)^5 \, dx$

e $\int x^4 (\ln x)^2 \, dx$

f $\int \frac{x^2}{\sqrt{(1+x)^3}} \, dx$

2 Evaluate these integrals.

a $\int_0^{\frac{\pi}{2}} 3x^2 \sin\left(2x + \frac{\pi}{2}\right) dx$

b $\int_0^1 (1-2x)^2 e^{-x} \, dx$

c $\int_{\frac{1}{2}}^{\frac{e}{2}} \frac{(\ln 2x)^2}{\sqrt{x}} \, dx$

3 Obtain $\int (\ln x)^2 \, dx$

Exercise 3M Integration by parts (repeating integral type)

1 Find these integrals.

a $\int e^{2x} \sin x \, dx$

b $\int e^{-x} \cos 4x \, dx$

c $\int \sin 2x \sin 3x \, dx$

d $\int \frac{\tan^{-1} 2x}{1 + 4x^2} \, dx$

2 Find the exact values of these integrals.

a $\int_{\frac{\pi}{2}}^{\pi} \cos 4x \sin x \, dx$

b $\int_0^{\frac{\sqrt{3}}{2}} \frac{\sin^{-1} x}{\sqrt{1 - x^2}} \, dx$

3 Use the substitution $x = \cos u$ to obtain $\int e^{\cos^{-1} x} \, dx$

1 Part of the graph of the curve $y = \dfrac{3}{1+2x}$ is shown in the diagram.

The region enclosed between this curve, the coordinate axes and the line $x = 2$ is shaded.

Find the exact area of the shaded region.

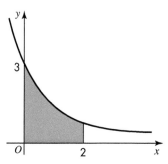

2 The diagram shows the graphs of the curves $y = e^{2x}$ and $y = 3e^x$.

The graphs of the curves intersect at the point A.

a Show that the x-coordinate of A is $\ln 3$.

b Hence find the area of the region enclosed between the two curves and the y-axis.

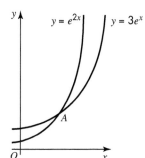

3 The acceleration, $a\,\mathrm{ms^{-2}}$, of a bicycle during the first several seconds of its journey is modelled by the equation

$$a(t) = 1 + \sqrt[3]{t-1}$$

where t is the number of seconds elapsed since the beginning of the journey.

Given that the bicycle starts at rest, find

a the velocity of the bicycle after two seconds

b the displacement of the bicycle after nine seconds, correct to 3 significant figures.

4 Part of the graph of the curve $y = \dfrac{1}{\sqrt{2+2x^2}}$ is shown in the diagram.

A fruit bowl is designed by rotating this curve for $0 \leqslant x \leqslant \dfrac{\pi}{3}$ completely around the x-axis.

Given that one unit represents 10 centimetres, find the capacity of the bowl to the nearest cm³.

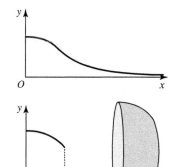

5 Part of the curve with equation $e^{2y} = \dfrac{x^2}{y}$ is shown in the diagram.

A solid is formed by rotating the curve, for $0 \leqslant y \leqslant 1$, through 2π radians around the y-axis.

Find the volume of the solid.

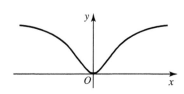

Chapter review

1 Find these integrals.

a $\int \left(2\sqrt{x} - \sin 6x + 3\right)dx$ **b** $\int \frac{5}{x^2 + 2}dx$

c $\int \frac{dx}{8x + 3}$ **d** $\int \frac{2}{\sqrt{5 - 3x^2}}dx$

e $\int 3x^2 e^{x^3 + 1} dx$ **f** $\int 6x \cos 3x \, dx$

g $\int \frac{2 - 5x}{x(x + 2)}dx$ **h** $\int \sin^3 4x \, dx$

i $\int (3x + 1)^2 e^{4-x} dx$ **j** $\int \frac{2x^2 - x + 9}{(x + 1)(x^2 + 3)}dx$

2 Evaluate these integrals.

a $\int_{-\pi}^{\pi} \cos\left(\frac{\pi - x}{4}\right)dx$ **b** $\int_0^1 \frac{10}{\sqrt{4 - x^2}}dx$

c $\int_1^e \sqrt{x} \, \ln x \, dx$ **d** $\int_0^{\ln 2} e^x \sin(e^x - 1)dx$

e $\int_0^{\frac{3}{\sqrt{2}}} \frac{7}{9 + 2x^2} dx$ **f** $\int_0^{\frac{\pi}{3}} (1 + \tan x)^2 \, dx$

g $\int_0^{\frac{\pi}{6}} \cos 5x \cos 2x \, dx$ **h** $\int_{\frac{\pi}{8}}^{\frac{\pi}{6}} \frac{\cos 2x}{1 - \sin 2x} dx$

i $\int_1^2 \frac{3x^2 + 3x - 1}{x^3 + 2x^2 + x}dx$ **j** $\int_0^2 \frac{2x^3}{x^2 + 3} dx$

3 Given that $f'(x) = 4\sec^2\left(\frac{x}{2}\right) - 1$ and $f\left(\frac{\pi}{2}\right) = 7$, find $f(x)$ in terms of x.

4 Use the substitution $u = \tan x$ to obtain $\int \frac{\sqrt{\tan x}}{\sin 2x} dx$

5 Use the substitution $u = \sqrt{x}$ to evaluate $\int_0^{\pi^2} \sin \sqrt{x} \, dx$

6 The velocity, v m s^{-1}, of a particle moving along a straight line after t seconds is given by

$$v(t) = \frac{1}{3}t^2 - 2t$$

Find the displacement of the particle after 3 seconds given that, initially, the object is at O.

7 **a** Write $\frac{x}{x + 2}$ in the form $a + \frac{b}{x + 2}$

b Use integration by parts to obtain $\int \ln(x + 2)dx, \, x > -2$

8 The diagram shows part of the graph of the parabola $y = 1 + x^2$.

A and B are the points $(0, 1)$ and $(2, 5)$ respectively.

Find the volume of the solid formed when the arc AB is rotated 360° around

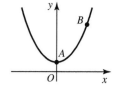

a the x-axis

b the y-axis.

9 a Differentiate $y = a^x$ where a is a positive constant.

b Hence obtain $\int a^x \, dx$

c Find the exact value of $\int_1^3 2^x \, dx$

4 Complex numbers

Exercise 4A Arithmetic of complex numbers

1 Evaluate these expressions, writing your answers in the form $a + bi$.

   a $(1 + 6i) + (2 + 4i)$ **b** $8i - (2 - i)$ **c** $7 + (6 - 9i)$

   d $(3 - 5i) - (-3 + 7i)$ **e** $i(2 + 5i)$ **f** $(3 + 4i) \times (9 + 2i)$

   g $(-4 + i) \times (9 - 2i)$ **h** $(8 - 3i)^2$ **i** $(3 + 2i) + (4 - i) \times (5 + 5i)$

2 Write each equation in the form in the form $a + bi$.

   a i^9 **b** $(3i)^6$ **c** $(-4 + i)^3$

   d $(3 - 5i)^4$ **e** $(2 + 3i)^5$ **f** $(1 - i)^6$

3 Solve each equation for z.

   a $z - 2 + 3i = 5 + i$ **b** $\dfrac{z}{9 - i} = 2 + 2i$ **c** $2 - z = 4 + 2i$

   d $\dfrac{2z}{3 + 3i} = (5 + i)^2$ **e** $3 - \dfrac{z}{1 - 3i} = 2 - i$ **f** $3 = \dfrac{(1 + i)^3}{z}$

Exercise 4B Division and square roots of complex numbers

1 Write down the complex conjugate of:

   a $1 + 6i$ **b** $-3 + 4i$ **c** $5 - 2i$ **d** $-2 - 4i$

   e 5 **f** $7i$ **g** $-i$ **h** -12

2 Evaluate these expressions, writing your answer in the form $a + bi$.

   a $6 \div (1 + i)$ **b** $(2 + 5i) \div (3 + i)$ **c** $(6 - 2i) \div i$

   d $\dfrac{-2 + 19i}{5 + 4i}$ **e** $\dfrac{10 - 30i}{7 - i}$ **f** $(3 - 4i)^{-1}$

   g $\dfrac{(2 - 5i)^2}{2 + i}$ **h** $\dfrac{4}{1 + 2i} - \dfrac{i}{1 + 3i}$ **i** $(2 - 3i)^{-2}$

3 Given that $z_1 = 4 - 3i$ and $z_2 = -2 + i$, evaluate:

   a $3z_1 + 2\bar{z}_2$ **b** $\bar{z}_1 z_2$ **c** $\bar{z}_2^{\,2} - 4z_1$

   d $\dfrac{\bar{z}_1}{2z_2}$ **e** $\left(z_2 - \bar{z}_2\right)^4$ **f** $\sqrt{z_1 \bar{z}_1}$

   g $\overline{5z_1 + z_2}$ **h** $\overline{z_1 \bar{z}_2}$ **i** $\overline{\left(\dfrac{z_2}{z_1}\right)}$

4 Solve each equation for z.

   a $z(1 - 2i) = 5 - 3i$ **b** $\dfrac{6}{z} = 12i$ **c** $\dfrac{z}{1 - i} + \dfrac{2z}{i} = 5$

   d $2z + \bar{z} = 9 + 5i$ **e** $\bar{z} - 3z = 4i$ **f** $4z + 2\bar{z} - i = 10$

   g $\bar{z}^2 - 4 = 20 + 10i$ **h** $z^2 = \bar{z}$ **i** $(2 + i)(z + 3i) = 10 - 5i$

5 Find the value of z given that $z^2 - \bar{z} + 1 = 0$ and $\text{Im}(z) < 0$

 6 **a** Write down the square roots of -4.

b Find the square roots of $-3 + 4i$

c Solve $z^2 = 8 - 6i$

d Solve $z^2 = i$

Exercise 4C Argand diagrams and polar form

 1 Represent each of these numbers on an Argand diagram.

a $5 + 2i$ **b** $-3 + i$ **c** 6 **d** $4 - 7i$

e $3i$ **f** $-i$ **g** -3 **h** $-6 - 6i$

2 Find the modulus, $|z|$, of each complex number.

a $z = 3 - 4i$ **b** $z = -5 + 12i$ **c** $z = 15 + 8i$

d $z = 5$ **e** $z = 1 - i$ **f** $z = 2 + 5i$

g $z = -3 - 3i$ **h** $z = -7i$ **i** $z = \sqrt{3} + i$

 3 Let $z_1 = a + bi$ and $z_2 = c + di$, where a, b, c and d are real numbers.

Prove that:

a $|z_1 z_2| = |z_1||z_2|$ **b** $\left|\dfrac{z_1}{z_2}\right| = \dfrac{|z_1|}{|z_2|}$

 4 Find the principal argument, arg z, of each complex number.

Give your answers to 3 significant figures where necessary.

a $z = 1 + i\sqrt{3}$ **b** $z = 5 + 5i$ **c** $z = 4$ **d** $z = -\sqrt{3} + i$

e $z = 1 - i$ **f** $z = 2i$ **g** $z = 7 + 2i$ **h** $z = -4 - 2i$

i $z = -8$ **j** $z = -3 + 3i$ **k** $z = -i$ **l** $z = 9 - 7i$

Hint To find the principal argument:

1 Plot the number on an Argand diagram. $z = a + bi$ has coordinates (a, b).

2 The principal argument depends on the quadrant in which z is located.

2nd quadrant	1st quadrant
$\arg z = \pi - \tan^{-1}\left|\dfrac{b}{a}\right|$	$\arg z = \tan^{-1}\left(\dfrac{b}{a}\right)$
$\arg z = \tan^{-1}\left|\dfrac{b}{a}\right| - \pi$	$\arg z = -\tan^{-1}\left|\dfrac{b}{a}\right|$
3rd quadrant	4th quadrant

3 Arguments for numbers in the 1st and 2nd quadrants are measured **anti-clockwise** from the positive direction of the real axis. Arguments for numbers in the 3rd and 4th quadrants are measured **clockwise** from the positive direction of the real axis. As a result, $-\pi < \arg z \leqslant \pi$.

5 Two complex numbers, ω and z, are given by $\omega = 2 + 2i$ and $z = -1 + \sqrt{3}i$.

  a Express ωz and $\dfrac{\omega}{z}$ in Cartesian form.

  b i By writing $\tan\left(\dfrac{\pi}{12}\right)$ as $\dfrac{\sin\left(\dfrac{\pi}{4} - \dfrac{\pi}{6}\right)}{\cos\left(\dfrac{\pi}{4} - \dfrac{\pi}{6}\right)}$, show that $\tan\left(\dfrac{\pi}{12}\right) = \dfrac{\sqrt{3} - 1}{\sqrt{3} + 1}$

  ii In a similar way, find the exact value of $\tan\left(\dfrac{5\pi}{12}\right)$

  c Verify that:

  i $\arg(\omega z) = \arg\omega + \arg z$ **ii** $\arg\left(\dfrac{\omega}{z}\right) = \arg\omega - \arg z$

6 Let k be a real number. Given that $\arg(3 + k + 4i) = \dfrac{\pi}{3}$, find the exact value of k.

7 Use the information provided to write z in:
  i polar form   **ii** Cartesian form.

  Give your answers to 3 significant figures where necessary.

  a $|z| = 2$, $\arg z = 60°$ **b** $|z| = \sqrt{2}$, $\arg z = 45°$

  c $|z| = 1$, $\arg z = 30°$ **d** $|z| = 8$, $\arg z = 120°$

  e $|z| = 5$, $\arg z = 23°$ **f** $|z| = 4$, $\arg z = -60°$

  g $|z| = \sqrt{3}$, $\arg z = \dfrac{\pi}{6}$ **h** $|z| = 2$, $\arg z = \dfrac{2\pi}{3}$

  i $|z| = 5\sqrt{2}$, $\arg z = -\dfrac{\pi}{6}$ **j** $|z| = 7$, $\arg z = \pi$

  k $|z| = 6$, $\arg z = -\dfrac{2\pi}{3}$ **l** $|z| = 3$, $\arg z = 0$

  > **Hint** When finding the principal argument, remember to plot the number on an Argand diagram first.

8 Write each complex number in polar form i.e. $r(\cos\theta + i\sin\theta)$ where $r > 0$ and $-\pi < \theta \leqslant \pi$.

  a $z = 4 + 4i$ **b** $z = 12$ **c** $z = -1 + \sqrt{3}i$

  d $z = 6 - 8i$ **e** $z = 8i$ **f** $z = -2 - 2i$

  g $z = 1 + 5i$ **h** $z = -3 + 4i$ **i** $z = -4$

  j $z = \sqrt{12} - 2i$ **k** $z = -5i$ **l** $z = -\sqrt{2} - i\sqrt{7}$

9 Given that $2(z + |z|) + \bar{z} = 1 - 4i$

  a Show that $\mathrm{Re}(z) < 0$ **b** Find the value of z.

Exercise 4D Multiplication and division of complex numbers in polar form

1 Evaluate each product, writing your answer in polar form.

a $4(\cos 35° + i\sin 35°) \times 3(\cos 20° + i\sin 20°)$

b $\sqrt{6}(\cos 57° + i\sin 57°) \times \sqrt{2}(\cos 62° + i\sin 62°)$

c $2(\cos 150° + i\sin 150°) \times (\cos 40° + i\sin 40°)$

d $8\left(\cos\dfrac{\pi}{4} + i\sin\dfrac{\pi}{4}\right) \times \dfrac{1}{2}\left(\cos\dfrac{\pi}{2} + i\sin\dfrac{\pi}{2}\right)$

e $\sqrt{50}\left(\cos\left(-\dfrac{\pi}{3}\right) + i\sin\left(-\dfrac{\pi}{3}\right)\right) \times \sqrt{2}\left(\cos\dfrac{\pi}{6} + i\sin\dfrac{\pi}{6}\right)$

f $2\sqrt{2}\left(\cos\left(-\dfrac{2\pi}{3}\right) + i\sin\left(-\dfrac{2\pi}{3}\right)\right) \times \sqrt{8}\left(\cos\left(-\dfrac{\pi}{4}\right) + i\sin\left(-\dfrac{\pi}{4}\right)\right)$

2 Evaluate each quotient, writing your answer in polar form.

a $\dfrac{14(\cos 45° + i\sin 45°)}{2(\cos 15° + i\sin 15°)}$

b $\dfrac{3(\cos 140° + i\sin 140°)}{6(\cos 90° + i\sin 90°)}$

c $\dfrac{\sqrt{20}(\cos 60° + i\sin 60°)}{\sqrt{5}(\cos 100° + i\sin 100°)}$

d $\dfrac{\cos\dfrac{\pi}{7} + i\sin\dfrac{\pi}{7}}{\cos\left(-\dfrac{\pi}{4}\right) + i\sin\left(-\dfrac{\pi}{4}\right)}$

e $\dfrac{15(\cos\pi + i\sin\pi)}{5\left(\cos\left(-\dfrac{\pi}{3}\right) + i\sin\left(-\dfrac{\pi}{3}\right)\right)}$

f $\dfrac{3\sqrt{2}\left(\cos\left(-\dfrac{\pi}{6}\right) + i\sin\left(-\dfrac{\pi}{6}\right)\right)}{3(\cos\pi + i\sin\pi)}$

> **Hint** Note that $\cos(-\theta) + i\sin(-\theta) = \cos\theta - i\sin\theta$

Exercise 4E de Moivre's theorem

1 Apply de Moivre's theorem to evaluate each expression.
Write your answers in polar form.

a $[3(\cos 70° + i\sin 70°)]^2$

b $[2(\cos 12° + i\sin 12°)]^7$

c $[5(\cos 65° + i\sin 65°)]^3$

d $[\cos(-135)° + i\sin(-135)°]^4$

e $\left[\sqrt{2}\left(\cos\dfrac{\pi}{8} + i\sin\dfrac{\pi}{8}\right)\right]^6$

f $\left[4\left(\cos\dfrac{2\pi}{3} + i\sin\dfrac{2\pi}{3}\right)\right]^3$

g $\left[2\sqrt{3}\left(\cos\left(-\dfrac{\pi}{4}\right) + i\sin\left(-\dfrac{\pi}{4}\right)\right)\right]^4$

h $[\cos 4 + i\sin 4]^7$

2 Apply de Moivre's theorem to evaluate each power.
Write your answers in Cartesian form.

a $(1 + \sqrt{3}i)^4$

b $(-2 + 2i)^5$

c $(6 + 2i)^6$

d $(2\sqrt{3} - i)^8$

e $(-3 - 2i)^4$

f $(-1 + i)^{12}$

3 Evaluate $\dfrac{(3 - 3i)^6(2 + 2\sqrt{3}i)^5}{(1 + i)^{10}}$, writing your answer in the form $a + bi$.

4 Let $z = \cos\theta + i\sin\theta$

    a Expand z^3 using: **i** de Moivre's theorem   **ii** the binomial theorem.

    b By equating real parts, prove that $\cos 3\theta \equiv \cos\theta\,(4\cos^2\theta - 3)$

    c By equating imaginary parts, prove that $\sin^3\theta \equiv \dfrac{1}{4}(3\sin\theta - \sin 3\theta)$

    d Hence obtain $\int \sin^3 x\,dx$

5 Let $z = \cos\theta + i\sin\theta$

    a Expand z^4 using: **i** de Moivre's theorem   **ii** the binomial theorem.

    b Show that $\cos 4\theta$ can be written in the form $p\cos^4\theta + q\cos 2\theta + r$ and state the values of integers p, q and r.

    c Hence:

        i evaluate $\displaystyle\int_0^{\frac{\pi}{2}} \cos^4 x\,dx$

        ii Show that $\dfrac{\cos 4\theta}{\cos^2\theta} = \alpha\cos^2\theta + \beta\sec^2\theta + \gamma$, where $-\dfrac{\pi}{2} < \theta < \dfrac{\pi}{2}$, stating the values of α, β and γ.

6 **a** Prove the identity $\cos 5\theta \equiv \cos^5\theta - 10\cos^3\theta\sin^2\theta + 5\cos\theta\sin^4\theta$

    b Find a similar identity for $\sin 5\theta$.

    c Use your results to show that $\tan 5\theta \equiv \dfrac{5\tan\theta - 10\tan^3\theta + \tan^5\theta}{1 - 10\tan^2\theta + 5\tan^4\theta}$

    d Hence verify that $\tan 300° = -\sqrt{3}$

Exercise 4F Roots of complex numbers

Example 4.1

Find the cube roots of $-26 + 18i$ and write them in Cartesian form.

$|-26 + 18i| = \sqrt{(-26)^2 + 18^2} = 10\sqrt{10}$

$\text{Arg}(-26 + 18i) = 180° - \tan^{-1}\left(\dfrac{18}{26}\right) \approx 145{\cdot}3°$ ⟵ Find the modulus and argument.

$-26 + 18i = 10\sqrt{10}\,(\cos 145{\cdot}3° + i\sin 145{\cdot}3°)$ ⟵ Write the number in polar form.

The cube roots of $-26 + 18i$ are given by

$z = \sqrt[3]{10\sqrt{10}}\left(\cos\left(\dfrac{145{\cdot}3 + 360k}{3}\right)^\circ + i\sin\left(\dfrac{145{\cdot}3 + 360k}{3}\right)^\circ\right)$ for $k = 0, 1, 2$ ⟵ Use de Moivre's theorem to find the cube roots. Remember there must be 3 answers.

$z_1 = \sqrt[3]{10\sqrt{10}}\left(\cos\left(\dfrac{145{\cdot}3}{3}\right)^\circ + i\sin\left(\dfrac{145{\cdot}3}{3}\right)^\circ\right) \approx 2{\cdot}10 + 2{\cdot}37i$

$z_2 = \sqrt[3]{10\sqrt{10}}\left(\cos\left(\dfrac{145{\cdot}3 + 360}{3}\right)^\circ + i\sin\left(\dfrac{145{\cdot}3 + 360}{3}\right)^\circ\right) \approx -3{\cdot}10 + 0{\cdot}63i$

$z_3 = \sqrt[3]{10\sqrt{10}}\left(\cos\left(\dfrac{145{\cdot}3 + 720}{3}\right)^\circ + i\sin\left(\dfrac{145{\cdot}3 + 720}{3}\right)^\circ\right) = 1 - 3i$ ⟵ Substitute $k = 0$, 1 and 2 and write in Cartesian form.

1 Solve each equation.

a $z^3 = 8(\cos 60° + i \sin 60°)$ **b** $z^4 = 81(\cos 140° + i \sin 140°)$

c $z^5 = \cos\left(-\dfrac{5\pi}{6}\right) + i\sin\left(-\dfrac{5\pi}{6}\right)$ **d** $z^6 = 8(\cos \pi + i \sin \pi)$

> **Hint** Remember that, since $\sin x$ and $\cos x$ are 2π-periodic, $z^n = r(\cos(\theta + 2k\pi) + i\sin(\theta + 2k\pi))$ where $k = 0, 1, 2, \ldots, n - 1$.

2 Solve:

a $z^4 = 16$ **b** $z^3 = -27$ **c** $z^2 = 21 + 20i$

d $z^3 = 2 - 11i$ **e** $z^6 = 1$ **f** $z^5 = -i$

3 **a** Find the fourth roots of $-7 - 24i$ in Cartesian form and illustrate them on an Argand diagram.

    b State the geometrical significance of these roots.

4 Find the fifth roots of unity in polar form and plot them on an Argand diagram.

Exercise 4G Solving polynomial equations

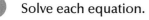

1 Solve each equation.

a $z^2 + 1 = 0$ **b** $z^2 + 2z + 5 = 0$ **c** $z^2 - 8z + 17 = 0$

d $4z^2 = 4z + 3$ **e** $5z^2 + 2z + 10 = 0$ **f** $3z^2 + 5 = 2z$

2 **a** Given that $z = 2$ is a root of the cubic equation $z^3 + 13z - 34 = 0$, find the other roots.

    b Given that $(z + 1)$ is a factor of $f(z) = z^3 - 5z^2 + 7z + 13$, solve the equation $f(z) = 0$

    c Show that $z = \dfrac{1}{2}$ is a root of the cubic equation $2z^3 + 11z = 3z^2 + 5$ and find the remaining roots.

    d Given that $z = 3 + i$ is a root of the equation $z^3 - 9z^2 + 28z - 30 = 0$

      i state another root

      ii find a quadratic factor of $z^3 - 9z^2 + 28z - 30$

      iii find the real root.

    e Given that $(z + 1 + \sqrt{3}i)$ is a factor of $f(z) = z^3 + 4z^2 + 8z + 8$, solve $f(z) = 0$

    f Verify that $z = 2i$ is a root of the cubic equation $3z^3 + 12z = 2z^2 + 8$ and then find the remaining roots.

> **Hint** Remember that complex roots of polynomial equations with real coefficients always come in complex conjugate pairs.

3 **a** Given that $z = -1 + i$ is a root of the equation $z^4 - 2z^3 + 7z^2 + 18z + 26 = 0$

    i state another root

    ii express $z^4 - 2z^3 + 7z^2 + 18z + 26$ as a product of two quadratic factors

    iii find the remaining roots.

  b Given that $z = \frac{1}{2}\left(-1 + \sqrt{3}i\right)$ is a root of the quartic equation $z^4 + z^3 = 3z^2 + 4z + 4$, find the other roots and illustrate all four roots on an Argand diagram.

4 The polynomial, p, is given by $p(z) = 6z^4 - 25z^3 + 32z^2 + 3z - 10$

  a Use algebraic division to show that $(z^2 - 4z + 5)$ is a factor of $p(z)$

  b Hence solve the equation $p(z) = 0$

Exercise 4H – Loci in the complex plane

Example 4.2

Sketch the locus of complex numbers which satisfy $|z + 2| > |z - i|$

$|(x + iy) + 2| > |(x + iy) - i| \Rightarrow |(x + 2) + iy| > |x + (y - 1)i|$ — Replace z with $x + iy$ and group real and imaginary parts on both sides of the inequality.

$\sqrt{(x + 2)^2 + y^2} > \sqrt{x^2 + (y - 1)^2}$

$(x + 2)^2 + y^2 > x^2 + (y - 1)^2$ — Use the rule $|z| = \sqrt{x^2 + y^2}$ then square both sides.

$4x + 4 > -2y + 1$

$y > -2x - \frac{3}{2}$ — Simplify inequality and compare with $y = mx + c$

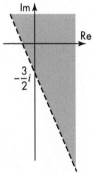

The locus is the set of points above the straight line through $-\frac{3}{2}i$ with gradient -2 in the complex plane.

1 Describe the locus of complex numbers given by each equation.

  a $|z| = 4$

  b $|z + 1| = |z - 3|$

  c $|z - i| = 5$

  d $|z + 1 - 2i| = 2$

  e $|z - i| = |z + i|$

  f $\frac{10z}{\bar{z}} = 6 + 8i$

> **Hint** Replace z with $x + iy$, group real and imaginary parts, square both sides to eliminate the square root sign(s) and then interpret the resulting equation – often a circle or a straight line.

2 Sketch each locus in the complex plane.

a $|z - 1| < 2$ **b** $1 < |z| < 4$ **c** $|z - i| \leqslant |z + 5i|$

d $\arg z = \dfrac{\pi}{4}$ **e** $\dfrac{\pi}{3} < \arg z < \dfrac{2\pi}{3}$ **f** $\operatorname{Re}(z) = 4$

g $\operatorname{Re}(z) + \operatorname{Im}(z) = 0$ **h** $\{z : z \in \mathbb{C}, -2 < \operatorname{Re}(z) < 4 \quad \text{and} \quad 3 < \operatorname{Im}(z) < 5\}$

Chapter review

1 Let $z_1 = 2 + i$, $z_2 = -3 - 4i$ and $z_3 = 5 - 2i$.

Evaluate:

a $z_1^2 + 2z_2 - 5$ **b** $\left|\dfrac{z_3}{z_1}\right|$ **c** $|z_2^2 + z_3^2|$

d $\left(z_2 - \overline{z_3}\right)^2$ **e** $\operatorname{Im}(z_1 z_2)$ **f** $\operatorname{Re}(2z_2^3)$

g $\sqrt{\overline{z_2}}$ **h** $\overline{(z_2 + z_3)(z_1 - z_3)}$ **i** z_1^4

2 Let $z = 1 + 2i$. Plot on an Argand diagram:

a z **b** $\overline{z}$ **c** $2z$

d $-z$ **e** $\dfrac{1}{z}$ **f** z^2

3 Solve each equation to find the value(s) of z in the form $a + bi$.

a $4z + 5 - 6i = 3 + 2i$ **b** $3z - 2\overline{z} = 5 + 60i$

c $z^2 - 3z + 3 = 0$ **d** $z^3 - z^2 + 3z + 5 = 0$

4 Given that $z_1 = 6\left(\cos \dfrac{\pi}{4} + i\sin \dfrac{\pi}{4}\right)$ and $z_2 = 2\left(\cos \dfrac{\pi}{6} + i\sin \dfrac{\pi}{6}\right)$, find, in Cartesian form:

a $z_1 z_2$ **b** $\dfrac{z_1}{z_2}$ **c** z_1^4 **d** z_2^7

5 a Write each expression in polar form.

i $-1 - i$ **ii** $\dfrac{\sqrt{3}}{2} + \dfrac{1}{2}i$ **iii** $3 - 3i$

b Hence evaluate $\dfrac{(3 - 3i)^3}{(-1 - i)^5\left(\dfrac{\sqrt{3}}{2} + \dfrac{1}{2}i\right)^4}$

6 a Expand $(\cos\theta + i\sin\theta)^3$ using

  i de Moivre's theorem   **ii** the binomial theorem.

b By equating real parts, show that $\cos^3\theta \equiv \frac{1}{4}(\cos 3\theta + 3\cos\theta)$

c Expand $(\cos\theta + i\sin\theta)^4$ using

  i de Moivre's theorem   **ii** the binomial theorem.

d By equating imaginary parts, show that $\dfrac{\sin 4\theta}{\sin\theta} \equiv 8\cos^3\theta - 4\cos\theta$

e Hence obtain $\displaystyle\int \frac{\sin 4\theta}{\sin\theta}\, d\theta$

7 a Given that $-1 = \cos\theta + i\sin\theta$, $-\pi < \theta \leqslant \pi$, state the value of θ.

b i Use de Moivre's theorem to find the non-real roots, z_1 and z_2, of the equation $z^3 + 1 = 0$.

  ii Hence show that $z_1^2 = -z_2$ and $z_2^2 = -z_1$

c Plot all of the roots of the equation $z^3 + 1 = 0$ on an Argand diagram and state their geometric significance.

8 Given that $z_1 = 2\left(\cos\dfrac{\pi}{6} + i\sin\dfrac{\pi}{6}\right)$ is a root of the equation $z^6 = \alpha$ where $\alpha \in \mathbb{R}$:

a find the value of α

b write down the other roots in polar form

c convert the roots to Cartesian form and illustrate them in the complex plane.

9 a Given that $z = 1 + i$ is a zero of the equation $z^4 + z^3 - 8z^2 + 14z - 8 = 0$, find the other zeros.

b i Verify that $z = \dfrac{3}{2} + \dfrac{\sqrt{7}}{2}i$ is a solution of the equation $z^2(1 - z^2) = 16$.

  ii Hence find the other solutions.

10 A function, f, is defined by $f(z) = z^5 - 2z^4 - z^3 + 6z - 4$ where $z \in \mathbb{C}$.

a Show that $f(-1 + i) = 0$.

b Hence find the roots of the equation $f(z) = 0$.

11 Sketch the locus given by:

a $|z + 2| = 3$ **b** $|z - 2 - 2i| = |z|$ **c** $z + \bar{z} = 8$

d $|z + 2i| \geqslant 2$ **e** $\mathrm{Im}(z) > -1$ **f** $3 \leqslant \mathrm{Re}(z) < 6$

g $\left\{z : z \in \mathbb{C}, 1 \leqslant |z| \leqslant 4 \quad\text{and}\quad \dfrac{\pi}{2} \leqslant \arg z \leqslant \dfrac{3\pi}{4}\right\}$

5 Differential equations

Exercise 5A First order differential equations (variables separable type)

Example 5.1

Find the general solution of the differential equation $(x + 3)\dfrac{dy}{dx} = 4e^y$

$\displaystyle\int e^{-y} \, dy = \int \dfrac{4}{x + 3} \, dx$ ⟵ Separate the variables and integrate both sides.

$-e^{-y} = 4\ln|x + 3| + c$ ⟵ Add a constant of integration to one side.

$e^{-y} = -4\ln|x + 3| - c$

$-y = \ln\big(-4\ln|x + 3| - c\big)$

$y = -\ln\big(-4\ln|x + 3| - c\big)$ or $y = -\ln(C - \ln(x + 3)^4)$ where $C = -c$ ⟵ Make y the subject.

1 Find the general solution for each of these first-order differential equations.

a $2\dfrac{dy}{dx} = x^3 y$

b $\dfrac{dy}{dx} = \sqrt{x}\sec y$

c $\dfrac{dy}{dx} = \dfrac{2x\sin^2 y}{1 + x^2}$

d $(2 - x)^2 \dfrac{dy}{dx} = 2y - 1$

e $\dfrac{dy}{dx} = 2\sqrt{4 - y^2}\cos^2 x$

f $e^y\sqrt{1 - x^2}\sin^{-1}x\dfrac{dy}{dx} = 1$

g $e^{2x}\dfrac{dy}{dx} = x\tan y$

h $x\dfrac{dy}{dx} = y(1 - y)$

2 Find the particular solution for each of these first-order differential equations.

a $\dfrac{dy}{dx} = 6x^2 y^2$ given that $y = 1$ when $x = 1$

b $\dfrac{dy}{dx} = e^{2x}(4 + y^2)$ given that $y = 2\sqrt{3}$ when $x = 0$

c $\sin y\dfrac{dy}{dx} = x\cos y$ given that $y = \dfrac{\pi}{4}$ when $x = 0$

d $\dfrac{dy}{dx} = \dfrac{y - 4}{x + 3}$ given that $y = 20$ when $x = 5$

e $x\ln x\dfrac{dy}{dx} = y(1 + \ln x)$ given that $y = 2e$ when $x = e$

f $y\dfrac{dy}{dx} - 2x = 3\dfrac{dy}{dx} - 5$ given that $y = 7$ when $x = 6$

g $\sin 2x\tan 2x\dfrac{dy}{dx} = y^2$ given that $y = \dfrac{\sqrt{2}}{5}$ when $x = \dfrac{\pi}{8}$

h $\dfrac{dy}{dx} = \sqrt{y}\sin 3x\cos 3x$ given that $y = 4$ when $x = \dfrac{\pi}{6}$

3 A radioactive substance decays according to the differential equation

$$\frac{dN}{dt} = -kN$$

where N is the number of grams present after t years and k is a positive constant.

a Given that, when $t = 0$, $N = 250$, express N as a function of t.

b After 10 years, 240 grams of the substance remains.

Find the value of k correct to 3 significant figures.

c How long will it take for 99% of the substance to decay?

4 Liquid leaks through a small hole at the base of a cylindrical container.

The depth, D cm, of the liquid inside the container after t minutes, decreases according to the differential equation

$$\frac{dD}{dt} = -\lambda\sqrt{D}$$

where λ is a positive constant.

Initially, the depth of the liquid in the container is 20 cm.

a Find the general solution of the differential equation.

b Given that, after 5 minutes, the depth of the liquid is 16 cm, find the value of the constant λ to 3 significant figures.

c Hence estimate, to the nearest millimetre, the amount of liquid in the container after a further 5 minutes.

d How much longer will it take, to the nearest minute, for the depth of the liquid to drop to 1 cm?

5 The pressure, P, of a gas varies with the volume, V, in which the gas is enclosed according to the differential equation

$$\frac{dP}{dV} = -\frac{kP}{V}$$

where k is a positive constant.

Find the general solution of the differential equation.

6 The boiling point, T, of a liquid under external pressure, P, is governed by the differential equation

$$\frac{dT}{dP} = \frac{\mu T^2}{\lambda P}$$

where λ and μ are constants.

Find the general solution of this differential equation.

7 Given that $\frac{dy}{dt} = \frac{\sec y}{4e^{3t}}$ and that $y = \frac{\pi}{6}$ when $t = 0$, find y in terms of t.

8 **a** Show that $\frac{d}{dx}\{\ln(\operatorname{cosec} x - \cot x)\} = \operatorname{cosec} x$

b Given that $\sin x \frac{dy}{dx} = \sqrt{4 - y^2}$ and that $y = 1$ when $x = \frac{\pi}{3}$, find y in terms of x.

9 In a town with a population of 40 000 people, a flu virus spread rapidly last winter. The percentage, P, of the population infected t days after the start of the outbreak increased at a rate proportional to the percentage already infected.

a Write down a differential equation to model the spread of the flu virus.

b Given that 100 people were infected initially find an expression for the percentage infected after t days.

c After 1 week, there were 500 people infected.

How many people are expected to be infected after a further 3 days?

Exercise 5B First order differential equations (integrating factor type)

Example 5.2

Find the particular solution of the differential equation $\dfrac{dy}{dx} + y\cos x = \cos x$ given that, when $x = 0$, $y = 3$.

$$\text{IF} = e^{\int \cos x\,dx} = e^{\sin x}$$

If $\dfrac{dy}{dx} + P(x)y = Q(x)$, the integrating factor, IF $= \exp\left(\int P(x)\,dx\right)$

$$e^{\sin x}\dfrac{dy}{dx} + e^{\sin x}y\cos x = e^{\sin x}\cos x$$

Multiply the differential equation through by the IF.

$$\Rightarrow \dfrac{d}{dx}\{e^{\sin x}y\} = e^{\sin x}\cos x$$

The LHS of the differential equation always simplifies to $\dfrac{d}{dx}\{\text{IF} \times y\}$.

$$\Rightarrow e^{\sin x}y = \int e^{\sin x}\cos x\,dx$$

Integrate both sides.

$$e^{\sin x}y = e^{\sin x} + c$$

Don't forget the constant of integration.

$$e^{\sin 0} \times 3 = e^{\sin 0} + c \Rightarrow c = 2$$

Substitute initial conditions to find the value of the constant.

$$e^{\sin x}y = e^{\sin x} + 2$$

Replace the constant in the general solution above with its correct value.

$$y = 1 + 2e^{-\sin x}$$

Make y the subject to give the particular solution.

1 Find a general solution for each of these first-order differential equations.

a $\dfrac{dy}{dx} + \dfrac{y}{x} = 3x$

b $\dfrac{dy}{dx} - \dfrac{y}{x} = 2\sqrt{x}$

c $\dfrac{dy}{dx} + y\tan x = 2\sec x$

d $\dfrac{dy}{dx} + 2y\cot 2x = 4\sin 2x$

e $\dfrac{dy}{dx} + \dfrac{y}{x} = e^{2x}$

f $\dfrac{dy}{dx} + y\cos x = \cos x$

g $\dfrac{dy}{dx} + y\ln x = \left(\dfrac{e^4}{x}\right)^x$

h $x(1+x)\dfrac{dy}{dx} + y = 4$

> **Hint** 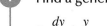 If necessary, first divide through by the coefficient of $\dfrac{dy}{dx}$ so that the equation is in the form $\dfrac{dy}{dx} + P(x)y = Q(x)$. The integrating factor is $e^{\int P(x)\,dx}$

2 Find the particular solution for each of these first-order differential equations.

a $\dfrac{dy}{dx} - \dfrac{y}{x^2} = e^{-\frac{1}{x}}$ given that $y = 0$ when $x = 1$

b $x\dfrac{dy}{dx} + 2y = x^4 + 1$ given that $y = 1$ when $x = 1$

c $(1 + \cos x)\dfrac{dy}{dx} - y\sin x = \sin x$ given that $y = 2$ when $x = \dfrac{\pi}{3}$

d $\cos x\dfrac{dy}{dx} + y\sin x = 1 + \sin x$ given that $y = 3$ when $x = 0$

e $\dfrac{dy}{dx} - xy = x$ given that $y = 0$ when $x = 0$

f $x(1 - x)\dfrac{dy}{dx} + y = 2$ given that $y = 4$ when $x = 2$

3 **a** Show that $\dfrac{\sec^2 A}{\tan A} \equiv 2\,\text{cosec}\,2A$

b Hence find the general solution of $\sin 2x\dfrac{dy}{dx} + 2y = 2\sin^2 x$

4 **a** Express $\dfrac{2 - x^2}{x(1 + x^2)}$ in terms of partial fractions.

b Use the substitution $u = 1 + x^2$ to show that $\displaystyle\int \dfrac{x^3}{\sqrt{1 + x^2}}\,dx = \dfrac{1}{3}(x^2 - 2)\sqrt{1 + x^2} + c$

c Find the particular solution of the differential equation

$$x(1 + x^2)\dfrac{dy}{dx} + (2 - x^2)y = x^2(1 + x^2)^2$$

given that, when $x = \sqrt{2}$, $y = 0$

5 **a** Show that the differential equation

$$2\sqrt{x}\dfrac{dy}{dx} + y = 2x$$

can be reduced to

$$e^{\sqrt{x}}y = \int \sqrt{x}e^{\sqrt{x}}\,dx$$

b Hence use the substitution $u = \sqrt{x}$ to find the general solution of the differential equation.

c Find the particular solution given that $y = 4$ when $x = 4$.

6 The differential equation

$$L\dfrac{dI}{dt} + RI = E$$

occurs in electrical theory, with L, R and E being positive constants.

a Given that $I = 0$ when $t = 0$, find I as a function of t.

b Hence explain why as $t \to \infty$, $I \to \dfrac{E}{R}$

Find a general solution for each of these second-order differential equations.

a $\dfrac{d^2y}{dx^2} - 2\dfrac{dy}{dx} = 0$

b $4\dfrac{d^2y}{dx^2} - 9y = 0$

c $\dfrac{d^2y}{dx^2} + 16y = 0$

d $\dfrac{d^2y}{dx^2} + 2\dfrac{dy}{dx} - 3y = 0$

e $4\dfrac{d^2y}{dx^2} + 4\dfrac{dy}{dx} + y = 0$

f $\dfrac{d^2y}{dx^2} - 3y = 0$

g $2\dfrac{d^2y}{dx^2} = 2\dfrac{dy}{dx} - y$

h $3\dfrac{d^2y}{dx^2} - \dfrac{dy}{dx} - 3y = 0$

> **Hint** If $a\dfrac{d^2y}{dx^2} + b\dfrac{dy}{dx} + cy = 0$, start with the auxiliary equation $am^2 + bm + c = 0$.
>
> The nature of the roots of the auxiliary equation lead to the form of the general solution.
>
> | Roots of auxiliary equation | General solution |
> |---|---|
> | Distinct real roots, m_1 and m_2 | $y = Ae^{m_1 x} + Be^{m_2 x}$ |
> | Repeated real roots, m | $y = (A + Bx)e^{mx}$ |
> | Imaginary roots, $\pm \beta i$ | $y = A\cos \beta x + B\sin \beta x$ |
> | Complex roots, $\alpha \pm \beta i$ | $y = e^{\alpha x}(A\cos \beta x + B\sin \beta x)$ |

 Find the particular solution for each of these second-order differential equations.

a $3\dfrac{d^2y}{dx^2} + 2\dfrac{dy}{dx} = 0$ given that, when $x = 0$, $y = 4$ and $\dfrac{dy}{dx} = 2$

b $\dfrac{d^2y}{dx^2} - 4y = 0$ given that, when $x = 0$, $y = 2$ and $\dfrac{dy}{dx} = -8$

c $\dfrac{d^2y}{dx^2} + 2y = 0$ given that $y(0) = \dfrac{1}{2}$ and $y\left(\dfrac{\pi\sqrt{2}}{8}\right) = \dfrac{5\sqrt{2}}{4}$

d $\dfrac{d^2y}{dx^2} - 9\dfrac{dy}{dx} + 14y = 0$ given that, when $x = 0$, $y = 3$ and $\dfrac{dy}{dx} = 31$

e $\dfrac{d^2y}{dx^2} - 6\dfrac{dy}{dx} + 9y = 0$ given that, when $x = 0$, $y = \dfrac{dy}{dx} = 1$

f $\dfrac{d^2y}{dx^2} + 5y = 2\dfrac{dy}{dx}$ given that, when $x = 0$, $y = 4$ and $\dfrac{dy}{dx} = 0$

g $\dfrac{d^2y}{dx^2} + \dfrac{dy}{dx} + 3y = 0$ given that, when $x = 0$, $y = 2$ and $\dfrac{dy}{dx} = 10$

h $9\dfrac{d^2y}{dx^2} - 12\dfrac{dy}{dx} + 4y = 0$ given that, when $x = 0$, $y = 3$ and when $x = \dfrac{3}{2}$, $y = -3e$

Exercise 5D Second order differential equations (non-homogeneous type)

Example 5.3

Find the general solution of the second order differential equation $\dfrac{d^2y}{dx^2} + 3\dfrac{dy}{dx} = x^2 - 6x + 1$

$m^2 + 3m = 0$

$m(m + 3) = 0$

$m = 0, m = -3$ — Write down and solve the auxiliary equation.

$y_{CF} = A + Be^{-3x}$ — The roots of the auxiliary equation give the form of the complementary function.

$y_{PI} \equiv px^2 + qx + r = x(px^2 + qx + r) = px^3 + qx^2 + rx$ — The particular integral has the same form as the RHS of the differential equation unless one or more of the terms shares the same form as the complementary function. In this case there is already a constant term in the complementary function. So, the particular integral is multiplied through by a factor, x. Now the CF and the PI do not have any like terms.

$\dfrac{dy_{PI}}{dx} = 3px^2 + 2qx + r$

$\dfrac{d^2y_{PI}}{dx^2} = 6px + 2q$ — Find the first and second derivatives of the particular integral.

$(6px + 2q) + 3(3px^2 + 2qx + r) = x^2 - 6x + 1$ — Substitute y_{PI}, $\dfrac{dy_{PI}}{dx}$ and $\dfrac{d^2y_{PI}}{dx^2}$ into the differential equation.

$9px^2 + (6q + 6p)x + (3r + 2q) = x^2 - 6x + 1$

$9p = 1, 6q + 6p = -6$ and $3r + 2q = 1$

$p = \dfrac{1}{9}, q = -\dfrac{10}{9}$ and $r = \dfrac{29}{27}$ — Equate coefficients to find the values of p, q and r.

$y_{PI} = \dfrac{1}{9}x^3 - \dfrac{10}{9}x^2 + \dfrac{29}{27}x$ — State the particular integral explicitly.

$y = A + Be^{-3x} + \dfrac{1}{9}x^3 - \dfrac{10}{9}x^2 + \dfrac{29}{27}x$ — The general solution is $y = y_{CF} + y_{PI}$.

1 Find the general solution for each of these second-order differential equations.

a $\dfrac{d^2y}{dx^2} - 4y = 5 - 8x - 4x^2$

b $\dfrac{d^2y}{dx^2} + y = 2x + 1$

c $\dfrac{d^2y}{dx^2} + 2\dfrac{dy}{dx} - 8y = \cos x - 47\sin x$

d $3\dfrac{d^2y}{dx^2} - 7\dfrac{dy}{dx} + 2y = 12e^x$

e $\dfrac{d^2y}{dx^2} - \dfrac{dy}{dx} = 3$

f $4\dfrac{d^2y}{dx^2} + y - 22 = 4\dfrac{dy}{dx} + 5x$

g $\dfrac{d^2y}{dx^2} - 2\dfrac{dy}{dx} - 3y = 16e^{3x}$

h $\dfrac{d^2y}{dx^2} - 4\dfrac{dy}{dx} + 4y = 6x^2 - 17$

2 Find the particular solution for each of these second-order differential equations.

a $3\dfrac{d^2y}{dx^2} - 5\dfrac{dy}{dx} = 34e^{2x}$ given that, when $x = 0$, $y = 8$ and $\dfrac{dy}{dx} = -24$

b $\dfrac{d^2y}{dx^2} - 2y = 2x^2$ given that, when $x = 0$, $y = \dfrac{3}{2}$ and $\dfrac{dy}{dx} = -\dfrac{5\sqrt{2}}{2}$

c $\dfrac{d^2y}{dx^2} + y = 6\cos x$ given that, when $x = 0$, $y = 4$ and $\dfrac{dy}{dx} = 1$

d $\dfrac{d^2y}{dx^2} - 8\dfrac{dy}{dx} + 16y = -e^{4x}$ given that $y(0) = -2$ and $y\left(\dfrac{1}{4}\right) = -\dfrac{e}{32}$

e $\dfrac{d^2y}{dx^2} - 2\dfrac{dy}{dx} + 5y + 5x = 13$ given that, when $x = 0$, $y = 2$ and $\dfrac{dy}{dx} = 0$

f $2\dfrac{d^2y}{dx^2} - 4\dfrac{dy}{dx} - 10y = 20 + 16x - 5x^2$ given that, when $x = 0$, $y = 1$ and $\dfrac{dy}{dx} = 0$

g $\dfrac{d^2y}{dx^2} + 2\dfrac{dy}{dx} + 3y = -\dfrac{1}{2}(19\sin 2x + 9\cos 2x)$ given that, when $x = 0$, $y = \dfrac{1}{2}$ and $\dfrac{dy}{dx} = 5$

h $9\dfrac{d^2y}{dx^2} + 6\dfrac{dy}{dx} + y = 14\sin x + 7$ given that, when $x = 0$, $y = 6$ and $\dfrac{dy}{dx} = 0$

Chapter review

1 Find the general solution for each of these differential equations.

a $\dfrac{dy}{dx} = 5y^3$

b $2\dfrac{d^2y}{dx^2} - 3\dfrac{dy}{dx} + y = 0$

c $\tan x\dfrac{dy}{dx} - y = 1$

d $\dfrac{d^2y}{dx^2} + y = 2\dfrac{dy}{dx}$

e $e^x\dfrac{dy}{dx} = \operatorname{cosec} y$

f $\dfrac{d^2y}{dx^2} + 16y = 5\sin 2x$

g $2x\dfrac{dy}{dx} - y = 6\sqrt{x^3}\sin^{-1}x$

h $\dfrac{d^2y}{dx^2} + \dfrac{dy}{dx} = 4x + 3 - e^{-x}$

2 Find the particular solution for each of these differential equations.

a $\dfrac{d^2y}{dx^2} - 3\dfrac{dy}{dx} = 10y + 60$ given that, when $x = 0$, $y = 9$ and $\dfrac{dy}{dx} = 26$

b $\dfrac{dy}{dx} = e^{-3y}\cos 2x$ given that $y = 0$ when $x = \dfrac{\pi}{4}$

c $\dfrac{d^2y}{dx^2} = 2\dfrac{dy}{dx} + 4y$ given that, when $x = 0$, $y = 1$ and $\dfrac{dy}{dx} = 1 - \sqrt{5}$

d $\dfrac{dy}{dx} - \dfrac{2xy}{x^2 + 4} - 1 = 0$ given that $y = \pi$ when $x = 2\sqrt{3}$

e $2\dfrac{d^2y}{dx^2} - 2\dfrac{dy}{dx} + 5y = 0$ given that, when $x = 0$, $y = -1$ and $\dfrac{dy}{dx} = 4$

f $10\dfrac{dy}{dx} = y^2 + 3y - 4$ given that $y = 6$ when $x = 0$

g $\dfrac{dy}{dx} + 2y = \cos 3x$ given that $y = 1$ when $x = 0$

h $\dfrac{d^2y}{dx^2} - 5\dfrac{dy}{dx} + 10y = 16\sin 3x - 14\cos 3x - 2e^x$ given that, when $x = 0$, $y = 1$ and $\dfrac{dy}{dx} = -4$.

3 The vertical speed, v km/h, of a rocket varies with its distance, r km, from the centre of the Earth according to the differential equation

$$\frac{dv}{dr} = -\frac{\rho}{r^2 v}$$

where $\rho > 0$ is a constant.

Find a formula for v in terms of r.

4 A particle is travelling along a straight line through a fixed origin O.
The displacement, x cm, of the particle after t seconds is governed by the differential equation:

$$\frac{dx^2}{dt^2} - \frac{dx}{dt} - 2x = 0$$

a Given that, initially, the particle is at O and has velocity $3\,\text{cm s}^{-1}$, find a formula for x in terms of t.

b Find the displacement of the particle after 4 seconds, correct to 3 significant figures.

5 A tub of water containing ice is left outdoors on a dry day.

The liquid water is evaporating but is also being formed by the melting ice.

The amount of liquid water, W ml, present after t minutes is given by

$$\frac{dW}{dt} + \alpha W = \beta e^{-\delta t}$$

where α, β and δ are positive constants.

a Find the general solution of the differential equation.

b Given that, initially, there was 800 ml of liquid water in the tub, show that the particular solution is given by

$$W = \frac{(800(\alpha - \delta) - \beta)e^{-\alpha t} + \beta e^{-\delta t}}{\alpha - \delta}$$

6 The vertical displacement, u, of an object attached to a spring is governed by the differential equation

$$\frac{d^2u}{dt^2} + \frac{du}{dt} - 6u = \alpha\sin\lambda t$$

where α and λ are real-valued constants and t represents time.

a Show that the particular integral is given by

$$u_{PI}(t) = -\frac{\alpha}{(\lambda^2 + 9)(\lambda^2 + 4)}\left((\lambda^2 + 6)\sin\lambda t + \lambda\cos\lambda t\right)$$

b Hence write down the general solution of the differential equation.

7 Two biologists each suggest a differential equation to model the growth of a particular type of cactus plant.

Model A $\dfrac{dh}{dt} = \dfrac{1}{h\sqrt{t}}$

Model B $(t + 1)\dfrac{dh}{dt} + h = \sqrt{(t + 1)^3}$

where h represents the height of the cactus, in cm, and t represents time, in weeks.

a Find the particular solution of each differential equation given that the cactus was initially 6 cm tall.

b After 4 weeks, the cactus was 6.5 cm tall. Which model appears to be the more accurate?

6 Functions and graphs

Exercise 6A Vertical asymptotes

1 Find the equations of any vertical asymptotes of the curves given by these equations.

a $y = \dfrac{x+2}{x-3}$

b $y = \dfrac{2x}{x+1}$

c $y = \dfrac{1}{2-3x}$

d $y = \dfrac{x+1}{x(x+2)}$

e $y = \dfrac{x^2}{x^2-9}$

f $y = \dfrac{2x^3}{4+x^2}$

g $y = \dfrac{x^2+x+1}{x^2+2x-3}$

h $y = \dfrac{4x-3}{x^3+4x^2-7x-10}$

2 Write down the equation of the vertical asymptotes of the curves given by these equations.

a $y = \ln(x-3)$

b $y = \ln(2x+1)$

c $y = 3\ln x + 1$

3 Find the equations of the vertical asymptotes of the curves given by these equations.

a $y = \tan 2x,\ -\pi \leqslant x \leqslant \pi$

b $y = \cot x,\ -2\pi \leqslant x \leqslant 2\pi,$

c $y = \sec\left(\dfrac{x}{2}\right),\ 0 \leqslant x \leqslant 2\pi$

4 Let $f(x) = (x^2 - p)(x^2 + qx + r)$

Constants p, q and r are such that:

- $p > 0$

- $q^2 < 4r$

Write down the equations of the vertical asymptotes on the graph of $y = \dfrac{1}{f(x)}$

Exercise 6B Horizontal asymptotes

1 Determine the equations of any horizontal asymptotes of the curves given by these equations.

a $y = \dfrac{5}{x+1}$

b $y = \dfrac{2x^2+1}{x^3}$

c $y = \dfrac{3x-2}{x+4}$

d $y = \dfrac{x^2-2}{x^2-x-3}$

e $y = \dfrac{x}{4x+5}$

f $y = \dfrac{3-2x}{5x}$

g $y = \dfrac{x^2-3}{x^3-3}$

h $y = \dfrac{3x^2}{x-1}$

> **Hint** Remember that, for rational functions, horizontal asymptotes occur only when degree (numerator) $\leqslant$ degree (denominator).

2 Write down the equations of the horizontal asymptotes of the curves given by these equations.

a $y = e^x + 2$

b $y = e^{-x} - 7$

c $y = ae^{bx} + c$, where a, b and c are positive constants.

3 The diagram shows part of the graph of the curve $y = 2\tan^{-1}3x$

Write down the equations of the horizontal asymptotes.

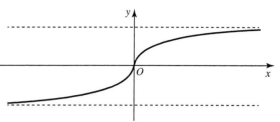

4 A curve has equation $y = \dfrac{p}{\sqrt[3]{x-q}}$, where p and q are real-valued constants.

Write down the equations of the vertical and horizontal asymptotes.

Exercise 6C Oblique asymptotes

1 Determine the equation of the oblique asymptotes of the curves given by these equations.

a $y = \dfrac{x^2 + 2x + 1}{x - 3}$

b $y = \dfrac{4x^2 + 12x - 1}{x + 3}$

c $y = \dfrac{(x + 5)(x - 2)}{2x - 1}$

d $y = \dfrac{1 - x^2}{x + 2}$

e $y = \dfrac{x^3 + x^2 - x - 6}{x^2 + 1}$

f $y = \dfrac{4x^3}{x^2 - 3x + 4}$

g $y = \dfrac{3x^2 - x + 1}{1 - 4x}$

h $y = \dfrac{3x(x + 4)(x - 1)}{(2x - 3)(x + 7)}$

2 Find the equations of any asymptotes of the curves given by these equations.

a $y = \dfrac{5}{2x + 3}$

b $y = \dfrac{x^2 + 1}{x - 2}$

c $y = \dfrac{x}{x^2 - 2}$

d $y = \dfrac{2x^3 + 1}{x^2 + 1}$

e $y = \dfrac{x^2 + 2}{x^2 - 5x + 4}$

f $y = \dfrac{1}{x^2 - x + 3}$

g $y = \dfrac{x^4 + 5x^2 - 3}{x^3 + 4x^2 + 6x + 24}$

h $y = \dfrac{3x^4 - x^3 + 2x^2 - 2}{4x^3 - 12x^2 + 5x + 6}$

3 A function, f, is defined by $f(x) = \dfrac{\alpha x^2}{(x - \beta)(x - \lambda)}$ where α, β and λ are non-zero integers.

a Write down the equations of the asymptotes on the graph of $y = f(x)$.

b Hence state the equations of the asymptotes on the graph $y = 2\,f(x + 4)$.

4 A curve has equation $y = \dfrac{ax^2 + bx + c}{x + 2}$ where a, b and c are constants with $a \ne 0$.

a Given that $(x + 2)$ is **not** a factor of $ax^2 + bx + c$, write down the equation of the vertical asymptote.

b The curve has the following properties:

- the graph crosses the y-axis at $(0, 2)$

- the oblique asymptote crosses the y-axis at $(0, 6)$

- $\dfrac{dy}{dx} \to 3$ as $x \to \pm\infty$

Find the values of a, b and c.

Exercise 6D Stationary points and their nature

1 Find the coordinates of any stationary points of the following curves and determine their nature.

a $y = x^3 - 5x^2 + 3x + 1$

b $y = x^3 - 3x^2 + 3x + 1$

c $y = 2x^3 + 3x^2 + 6x - 6$

d $y = \sqrt{x^2 + 2x + 2}$

e $y = \dfrac{1}{x^2 - 1}$

f $y = \dfrac{x + 2}{x - 2}$

g $y = \dfrac{4x^2 - 3}{x^3}$

h $y = \dfrac{4x}{(x - 2)^2}$

i $y = \dfrac{x^2 + 3x + 1}{x + 2}$

2 Find the coordinates of the stationary point on the curve $y = x \ln x$ and determine its nature.

3 Show that the graph of the curve $y = \cot x$ has no stationary points.

4 A function, f, is defined on a suitable domain by $f(x) = \sec x$.

a Find $f'(x)$ and $f''(x)$.

b Show that the graph of $y = f(x)$ has stationary points at $\left(k\pi, (-1)^k\right)$ $\forall k \in \mathbb{Z}$.

c By considering separately the cases where k is even and where k is odd, describe the natures of the stationary points.

Exercise 6E Points of inflection

Example 6.1

Find the coordinates of the point(s) of inflection on the graph of $y = x^4 - 6x^2 + 1$

$\dfrac{dy}{dx} = 4x^3 - 12x \Rightarrow \dfrac{d^2y}{dx^2} = 12x^2 - 12$ —— Find the second derivative.

Let $12x^2 - 12 = 0 \Rightarrow x = \pm 1$

Points of inflection occur when $\dfrac{d^2y}{dx^2} = 0$ or is undefined.

$12x^2 - 12$ is defined for all real values of x, so only consider the case where $\dfrac{d^2y}{dx^2} = 0$.

When $x = -1 \cdot 1$, $\dfrac{d^2y}{dx^2} > 0$

When $x = -0 \cdot 9$, $\dfrac{d^2y}{dx^2} < 0$.

Change of sign, so there is a point of inflection when $x = -1$.

When $x = 1 \cdot 1$, $\dfrac{d^2y}{dx^2} > 0$

Points of inflection occur when $\dfrac{d^2y}{dx^2}$ changes sign. To establish whether there are points of inflection at $x = -1$ and $x = 1$, substitute values above and below each of these values.

When $x = 0 \cdot 9$, $\dfrac{d^2y}{dx^2} < 0$.

Change of sign, so there is a point of inflection when $x = 1$.

When $x = \pm 1$, $y = -4$, so there are points of inflection at $(-1, 4)$ and $(1, 4)$. —— Find y-coordinates.

6 Functions and graphs

1 Find any points of inflection of the curves given by these equations.

  a $y = x^5$

  b $y = 9\sqrt[3]{x}$

  c $y = \frac{1}{3}x^3 - x^2 - 8x + 2$

  d $y = x^4 + 4x^3 - 18x^2 + 20x + 1$

  e $y = \frac{x}{1+x}$

  f $y = \frac{x^3 - x + 1}{x^2}$

  g $y = \frac{x^2 + x + 2}{x+1}$

  h $y = \frac{x}{x^3 - 1}$

2 Show that the graph of $y = \cot x$ has a non-horizontal point of inflection at $x = \frac{\pi}{2}$

3 Find the coordinates of the points of inflection on the graph of $y = 4x - \ln\sqrt{1 + x^2}$.

4 Find the coordinates of the points of inflection on the graph of $y = \sin^2 x,\ 0 \leqslant x \leqslant \pi$.

5 A curve has equation $y = ax^3 + bx^2 + cx + d$ where a, b, c and d are constants with $a \neq 0$.

  a Show that the curve has no stationary points when $b^2 < 3ac$.

  b Show that the curve has a point of inflection and determine its x-coordinate.

6 Three statements about the curve $y = \frac{e^x}{x}$ are given below.

Statement A: The curve does not intersect the coordinate axes.

Statement B: The curve has no stationary points.

Statement C: The curve has no points of inflection.

For each statement, decide whether it is true or false, giving clear explanations.

Exercise 6F Maximum and minimum values of functions on closed intervals

1 Determine the maximum and minimum values of each function over the given interval.

  a $y = x^2 - 4x + 3,\quad 0 \leqslant x \leqslant 4$

  b $y = \frac{1}{3}x^3 - x^2 - 3x + 5,\quad -4 \leqslant x \leqslant 4$

  c $y = x^x,\quad \frac{1}{3} \leqslant x \leqslant 2$

  d $y = (x - 1)^2\, e^{-x},\quad 0 \leqslant x \leqslant 5$

  e $y = \sin 2x - \cos 2x,\quad 0 \leqslant x \leqslant 2$

  f $y = \begin{cases} 1 - x, & x \leqslant 0 \\ x^2 - 2x + 1, & x > 0 \end{cases},\quad -3 \leqslant x \leqslant 3$

  g $y = \begin{cases} e^x, & x \leqslant 1 \\ \tan x, & x > 1 \end{cases},\quad -1 \leqslant x \leqslant \frac{3}{2}$

  h $y = \begin{cases} -\sin x, & x < 0 \\ \sqrt[3]{x}, & x \geqslant 0 \end{cases},\quad -2 \leqslant x \leqslant 2$

2 A function, f, is defined by $f(x) = x^2 - 2x + 3$, $x \in \mathbb{R}$

   a Find the minimum value of f.

   b Hence state the range of the function, g, defined by $g(x) = \dfrac{1}{f(x)}$

Exercise 6G Odd and even functions

 1 For each function, decide whether it is odd, even or neither.

   a $f(x) = 6x^4 + \cos x$ **b** $g(x) = 2x^3 + 1$

   c $h(x) = \dfrac{1}{3x} - 2x$ **d** $f(x) = \sin x^2 + 3\cos 2x$

   e $f(x) = \sqrt{x^4 + 4}$ **f** $g(x) = \dfrac{\sin x - x}{x^2}$

   g $f(x) = \cot x - 4x^5$ **h** $h(x) = x^3(e^x + e^{-x})$

> **Hint** Even functions have the property $f(-x) = f(x)$. The graph of an even function is symmetrical through the y-axis.
>
> Odd functions have the property $f(-x) = -f(x)$. The graph of an odd function has half-turn symmetry about the origin.

2 A function, f, is defined by $f(x) = \dfrac{2x}{\sqrt{x^2 + 1}}$ where $x \in \mathbb{R}$

   a Show that:

      i the curve $y = f(x)$ has no stationary points

      ii the curve $y = f(x)$ has a point of inflection at the origin

      iii As $x \to \infty$, $f(x) \to 2$

      iv f is an odd function.

   b Hence sketch the graph of the curve $y = f(x)$ showing clearly the behaviour of the curve as it approaches the asymptotes.

 3 Let f and g be odd functions.

   Prove that the function, h, defined by $h(x) = \dfrac{f(x)}{g(x)}$ is an even function.

4 The diagram shows the graph of $y = f(x)$ for $0 \leqslant x \leqslant b$

   The curve has the following properties:

   • $f(0) = 0$

   • $(a, f(a))$ is a maximum turning point

   • $\dfrac{dy}{dx} = 0$ at $x = 0$ and $x = a$

   • $y \to c$ as $x \to \infty$

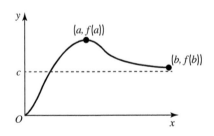

   Sketch the graph of $y = f(x)$ for $-b \leqslant x \leqslant b$ if:

   a f is even   **b** f is odd.

Exercise 6H Discontinuity

1 For each function, identify any values of x for which the function is discontinuous. Should a point of discontinuity exist, provide a reason for it.

a $y = \dfrac{3}{x - 2}$

b $y = \dfrac{x - 2}{x^2 - 1}$

c $y = \begin{cases} 2x, & x \leqslant 1 \\ x^2 + 1, & x > 1 \end{cases}$

d $y = \begin{cases} e^{-x}, & x \leqslant 0 \\ \sin x, & x > 0 \end{cases}$

e $y = \begin{cases} 3, & x \leqslant -1 \\ 2 - x, & x > -1 \end{cases}$

f $y = \begin{cases} 5 - x^2, & x < 1 \\ \ln x, & x \geqslant 1 \end{cases}$

g $y = \begin{cases} -x, & x < -3 \\ x^2 - 6, & -3 \leqslant x \leqslant 2 \\ \sqrt{x - 1}, & x > 2 \end{cases}$

h $y = \begin{cases} \dfrac{1}{x}, & x < 0 \\ \sec x, & 0 \leqslant x < \dfrac{\pi}{3} \\ 3 + \cos x, & x \geqslant \dfrac{\pi}{3} \end{cases}$

Exercise 6I Sketching graphs of rational functions

1 For each curve:

i find where its graph crosses the coordinate axes

ii identify the equations of any asymptotes

iii find the stationary points and determine their nature

iv sketch the curve.

a $y = \dfrac{x + 2}{x - 1}$

b $y = \dfrac{2x}{(x - 1)^2}$

c $y = \dfrac{x^2 + x + 2}{x + 3}$

d $y = \dfrac{8}{x^2 - x - 6}$

e $y = \dfrac{x^2 - 9}{2x^2 + 1}$

f $y = \dfrac{x(x - 4)}{x - 1}$

g $y = \dfrac{x^3}{6 + x - x^2}$

h $y = \dfrac{x^3 + 4x^2 - x - 4}{x^3}$

2 A curve has equation $y = \dfrac{x(x - 4)}{(x - 3)(x + 1)}$

a Find the coordinates of the points where the curve crosses the coordinate axes.

b Find the equations of any asymptotes.

c Show that there are no stationary points on the curve.

d Find $\dfrac{d^2y}{dx^2}$ and hence show that there is a point of inflection at $x \approx 1 \cdot 17$.

e Sketch the curve.

Exercise 6J Transformations of graphs

 1 The diagram shows part of the graph of the curve $y = f(x)$.

The graph has a:

- local maximum at $(0, 3)$
- local minimum at $(3, 0)$
- non-horizontal point of inflection at $(-2, 0)$.

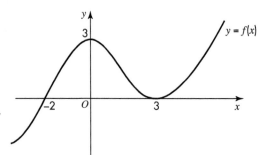

Sketch the graph of:

a $y = f(x - 1)$ **b** $y = 3 + f(x)$ **c** $y = f(-x)$ **d** $y = 2 f(x) - 1$

e $y = -f(x + 2)$ **f** $y = f\left(\dfrac{x}{2}\right)$ **g** $y = f'(x)$ **h** $y = 4 - f(2x - 3)$

 2 Sketch the graph of each curve.

For trigonometric functions, sketch the graph for $-2\pi \leqslant x \leqslant 2\pi$.

a $y = 2e^{-x}$ **b** $y = 4 - (x - 1)^2$ **c** $y = 3\cos 2x - 1$

d $y = \dfrac{1}{2}x^3 + 3$ **e** $y = \ln(1 - x)$ **f** $y = \tan\left(x - \dfrac{\pi}{2}\right) - 2$

g $y = 2 - e^{x + 2}$ **h** $y = \ln x^4$

 3 A curve has equation $y = f(x)$ where $f(x) = \dfrac{2x^2 - 7x + 14}{x - 2}$, $x \neq 2$

a i Show that the curve has no real roots.

  ii Find the coordinates of the y-intercept.

  iii Identify the equations of any asymptotes.

  iv Find the coordinates of the stationary points and determine their nature.

  v Sketch the curve.

b Let $g(x) = f(x + 2) - 1$.

  i Sketch the graph of $y = g(x)$.

  ii Verify algebraically that g is an odd function.

Exercise 6K Inverse functions and modulus functions

 1 For each function:

i Sketch the graph of $y = f(x)$.

ii Sketch the graph of the inverse function, $y = f^{-1}(x)$, on the same diagram.

a $f(x) = 3 - 2x$, $x \in \mathbb{R}$ **b** $f(x) = 2x^2 + 1$ for $x \geqslant 0$

c $f(x) = (x - 2)^3$, $x \in \mathbb{R}$ **d** $f(x) = \sin 2x$ for $-\dfrac{\pi}{4} \leqslant x \leqslant \dfrac{\pi}{4}$

e $f(x) = 2 - e^x$, $x \in \mathbb{R}$ **f** $f(x) = 2\tan x$ for $-\dfrac{\pi}{2} \leqslant x \leqslant \dfrac{\pi}{2}$

g $f(x) = \ln\left(\dfrac{x}{2}\right)$, $x > 0$ **h** $f(x) = \sqrt[5]{1 - x}$, $x \in \mathbb{R}$

2 For each graph:

  i sketch the graph of the inverse function, $y = f^{-1}(x)$

  ii sketch the graph of $y = |f(x)|$, clearly indicating the coordinates of any critical points.

a

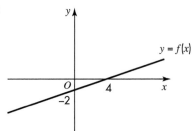

b

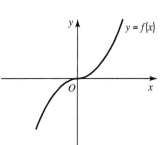

c

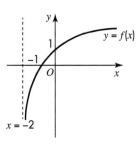

d

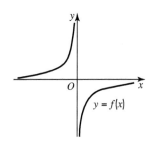

> **Hint** To sketch the graph of $y = f^{-1}(x)$, reflect the graph of $y = f(x)$ in the line $y = x$.

3 A function, f, is defined on the real numbers by $f(x) = \dfrac{1-x}{2+x}$, $x \neq -2$

  a For the curve with equation $y = f(x)$:

    i find the coordinates of the points of intersection with the x- and y-axes

    ii determine the equations of any asymptotes

    iii show that there are no stationary points on the curve

    iv sketch the graph.

  b Hence sketch the graph of:

    i $y = f^{-1}(x)$ **ii** $y = |f(x)|$ **iii** $y = |f^{-1}(x)|$

4 A curve has equation $y = \dfrac{ax}{b-x}$, where a and b are positive constants.

  a Write down the equations of the asymptotes of the curve.

  b Hence write down the equations of the asymptotes of the curve $y = \left|\dfrac{ax}{b-x} + c\right|$, where $0 < c < a$.

5 Sketch the graph of:

  a $y = |\ln x|$, $x > 0$ **b** $y = \ln|x|$, $x \neq 0$ **c** $y = |\ln|x||$, $x \neq 0$

6 Let $f(x) = e^x - 1$, $x \in \mathbb{R}$.

    a Sketch the graph of $y = f(x)$.

    b Find the exact value of:

        i $\displaystyle\int_0^1 f(x)\,dx$ **ii** $\displaystyle\int_{-1}^0 f(x)\,dx$

    c Hence write down the exact value of $\displaystyle\int_{-1}^1 |f(x)|\,dx$

Chapter review

1 Part of the graph of the curve $y = f(x)$ is shown in the diagram.

The graph has local extrema at $(-4, 0)$ and $(0, 4)$ and intersects the x-axis at $(2, 0)$.

On a similar diagram, sketch the graph of:

    a $y = \dfrac{1}{2}f(x - 4)$ **b** $y = 2 + f(-x)$ **c** $y = |f(2x)|$

    d $y = |1 - f(x)|$ **e** $y = f'(x)$ **f** $y = f(|x|)$

2 Sketch the graph of each of the given functions, showing all important features.

    a $y = \dfrac{x}{(x + 1)^2}$ **b** $y = \dfrac{x^2 + 5x + 5}{x + 3}$

    c $y = \dfrac{2x^3}{x^2 - 4}$ **d** $y = \left|\dfrac{x^2 - 2x - 8}{x^2 + 1}\right|$

3 Let $f(x) = \dfrac{k}{1 + x^2}$ where k is a positive constant.

Two other functions, g and h, are given by

    • $g(x) = f(x)\sin x$

    • $h(x) = f(x)\cos x$

    a Show that g is an odd function and that h is an even function.

    b Let $a > 0$.

        i Write down the value of $\displaystyle\int_{-a}^a g(x)\,dx$

        ii Given that $\displaystyle\int_0^a h(x)\,dx = A$, write down the value of $\displaystyle\int_{-a}^a h(x)\,dx$

4 A function, f, is given by $f(x) = x - 6 + \dfrac{12}{x + 1}$, $x \neq -1$

    a Sketch the graph of $y = f(x)$, showing clearly any stationary points, asymptotes and intersections with the coordinate axes.

    b Hence sketch the graph of $y = f'(x)$.

5 A curve has equation $y = x(x^3 + ax^2 + bx + c)$, where a, b and c are real-valued constants.

Prove that if the curve has at least one point of inflection then $3a^2 \geqslant 8b$.

6 A curve has equation $y = \dfrac{1}{\ln x}$, $x > 0$

a Write down the equation of the vertical asymptote on the curve.

b Explain why the curve has a horizontal asymptote and write down its equation.

c Show that the curve has no stationary points.

d Find $\dfrac{d^2y}{dx^2}$ and hence find the coordinates of the point of inflection.

d Sketch the graph of the curve, showing any important features.

7 A function, f, is defined by

$$f(x) = \begin{cases} 1 - x, & x < 0 \\ 1 - x^2, & x \geqslant 0 \end{cases}$$

a Sketch the graph of $y = f(x)$.

b Hence sketch the graph of the inverse function, $y = f^{-1}(x)$.

c i Express $f^{-1}(x)$ in terms of x.

ii Write down a similar expression for $\left|f^{-1}(x)\right|$

7 Sequences and series

Exercise 7A Arithmetic sequences

 1 For each arithmetic sequence, state the values of a (the 1st term) and d (the common difference) and then find a formula for u_n (the nth term).

a 4, 9, 14, 19, …

b 2, –1, –4, –7, …

c 3, 14, 25, 36, …

d $\frac{1}{2}$, 2, $\frac{7}{2}$, 5, …

e –10, –4, 2, 8, …

f $\frac{1}{4}$, $\frac{7}{12}$, $\frac{11}{12}$, …

 2 **a** An arithmetic sequence has a common difference of –2 and its 7th term is –4.

Find the 1st term of the sequence.

b The 1st term of an arithmetic sequence is 5 and the 8th term is 89.

Find the common difference and the 18th term of the sequence.

c An arithmetic sequence, $\{u_n\}$, has 1st term –7 and common difference 4.

Given that $u_k = 37$, find the value of k.

d The arithmetic sequence $\{u_n\}$ has $u_5 = -22$ and $u_{14} = -85$.

Find the value of u_{20}.

e Two arithmetic sequences are given.

$$-15, -12, -9, \dots$$

$$57, 51, 45, \dots$$

Find the value of n given that the nth terms of the two sequences are equal.

f In the arithmetic sequence, $\{u_n\}$, $u_1 = \sqrt{2}$ and $u_2 = \frac{3}{\sqrt{2}}$

Find u_{11}.

 3 The first three terms of an arithmetic sequence are

$$a, (a + 4) \text{ and } (2a + 1)$$

Find

a the value of a

b the common difference

c the 100th term.

4 In the arithmetic sequence 4·2, 4·9, 5·6, …, determine the first term to exceed 100.

5 An arithmetic sequence has 1st term a and common difference 3.

Given that the 7th term of the sequence is $10a$, find the value of a.

 6 The first three terms of an arithmetic sequence, with terms expressed in base k, are

$$6_k, 22_k \text{ and } 36_k$$

Find the value of k.

Exercise 7B Sum to n terms of an arithmetic series

1 Find a formula for the sum of the first n terms of each arithmetic series.

    a $3 + 7 + 11 + \ldots$ **b** $10 + 8 + 6 + \ldots$ **c** $-4 - 12 - 20 - \ldots$

    d $-4{\cdot}5 - 2 + 0{\cdot}5 + \ldots$ **e** $\sqrt{6} + 2\sqrt{6} + 3\sqrt{6} + \ldots$ **f** $\dfrac{1}{2} + \dfrac{3}{4} + 1 + \ldots$

2   **a** Find the sum of the first 30 terms of the arithmetic series $4 + 8 + 12 + \ldots$

    b Find the sum of the first 20 terms of the arithmetic series $2 - 3 - 8 - \ldots$

    c Find the sum of the first 50 terms of the arithmetic series whose 1st term is 6 and whose 50th term is 13.

3   **a** Find the sum of the arithmetic series $23 + 29 + 36 + \ldots + 149$.

    b Find the total of the arithmetic series $-1 - 3 - 5 - \ldots - 39$.

    c Find the sum of all the positive multiples of 8 which are less than 500.

    d Find the sum of all of the three-digit multiples of 9.

4 The sum of the first n terms of the arithmetic series $-7 - 3 + 1 + \ldots$ is 1025.
Find the value of n.

5 The 3rd term of an arithmetic series is 8 and the sum of the first 8 terms is -2.
Find the 1st term of the series and the common difference.

6 Let S_n denote the sum of the first n terms of an arithmetic series.
Given that $S_3 = -36$ and $S_7 = 28$, find S_{10}.

7 The nth term of an arithmetic sequence $u_1, u_2, u_3, \ldots$ is given by
$$u_n = 17 - 5n$$
Find a formula for S_n, the sum of the first n terms of the sequence.

8 The sum of the first n terms of the arithmetic sequence $u_1, u_2, u_3, \ldots$ is given by
$$S_n = \frac{1}{4}n(51 + 9n)$$
Find a formula for the nth term of the sequence.

9 The first two terms of an arithmetic sequence are 2 and 10.
After how many terms does the associated arithmetic series exceed 300?

Exercise 7C Geometric sequences

1 For each geometric sequence, state the values of a (the 1st term) and r (the common ratio) and then find a formula for u_n (the nth term) in its simplest form.

    a $2, 6, 18, \ldots$ **b** $5, 20, 80, \ldots$ **c** $-3, 6, -12, \ldots$

    d $20, 10, 5, \ldots$ **e** $18, -6, 2, \ldots$ **f** $2\sqrt{2}, 2, \sqrt{2}, \ldots$

2 **a** Find the 7th term of the geometric sequence 40, 30, 22·5, …

b Find the 30th term in the geometric sequence 2000, 2200, 2420, …

c The geometric sequence $\{u_n\}$ has a common ratio of 5 and $u_9 = 625$.
  Find the 1st term of the sequence.

d In the geometric sequence $\{u_n\}$, $u_5 = 32$ and $u_{12} = -4096$.
  Find the value of u_{15}.

e In the geometric sequence $\{u_n\}$, $u_4 = 2\cdot4$, $u_7 = 19\cdot2$ and $u_k = 614\cdot4$.
  Find the value of k.

f The first three terms of the geometric sequence, $\{u_n\}$, are 1, 1·5 and 2·25.
  Find the smallest value of n such that $u_n > 50$.

3 The 1st term of a geometric sequence is 4 and the 3rd term is 0·36.
Find the common ratio given that:

a the terms of the sequence are always positive

b the signs of the terms alternate.

4 Three consecutive terms of a geometric sequence are x, $3x - 3$ and $10x - 18$.
Find:

a the value(s) of x **b** the common ratio(s).

5 A geometric sequence has common ratio $\dfrac{3}{4}$

The kth term is x and the $(k + 2)$th term is $\left(\dfrac{1}{2}x + 3\right)$

Find the value of x.

6 Sophia opens a savings account and makes a deposit of £1500.

Assuming the interest rate of 2·6% doesn't change, what should the balance in the account be after 10 years?

7 The first Littleville Arts Festival attracted approximately 2450 visitors.

The following year, 2620 visitors attended the festival.

At this rate, after how many more years will the number of visitors exceed 5000?

8 An arithmetic sequence $\{u_n\}$ and a geometric sequence $\{v_n\}$ have the same 1st term.

The common difference of the arithmetic sequence is equal to the common ratio of the geometric sequence.

Let x be the value of the common difference of the arithmetic sequence.

a Show that, regardless of the value of the 1st term, there exists $x \in \mathbb{R}$ such that

  $u_3 = v_3$.

b Given that

  • $u_3 = v_3$

  • the 1st term of each sequence is 2

  • both sequences are made up of only positive terms

  write down the first three terms in each sequence.

9 An arithmetic sequence has 1st term a and common difference d where $d \neq 0$.

    a Write down expressions for first three terms of the sequence.

    b Prove that is impossible for these expressions to be the first three terms of a geometric sequence.

Exercise 7D Sum to n terms of a geometric series

1 Find a formula for the sum to n terms of each geometric series.

    a $4 + 12 + 36 + \ldots$ **b** $5 - 10 + 20 - \ldots$ **c** $216 + 180 + 150 + \ldots$

    d $1 + \sqrt{2} + 2 + \ldots$ **e** $72 - 36 + 18 - \ldots$ **f** $\dfrac{1}{12} + \dfrac{5}{48} + \dfrac{25}{192} + \ldots$

2   **a** Find the sum of the first 15 terms of the geometric series $1 + 5 + 25 + \ldots$

    b Find the sum of the first eight terms of the geometric series $4 + 6 + 9 + \ldots$

    c Find the sum of the first 10 terms of the geometric series $-12 - 6 - 3 - \ldots$

    d Find the sum of the geometric series $6 + 12 + 24 + \ldots + 24576$

    e Find the sum of the geometric series $18 + 9 + \ldots + \dfrac{9}{128}$

    f Find the sum of the geometric series $240 - 180 + 135 - \ldots - \dfrac{32805}{1024}$

3 The sum of the first n terms of a geometric series is given by $S_n = 3^n - 1$.

Find the 7th term in the series.

4 A geometric series has 1st term 14 and common ratio $\dfrac{6}{5}$.

Find n such that the sum of the first n terms is $75 \cdot 152$.

5 Let $S(n)$ denote the sum of the first n terms of the geometric series with 1st term a and common ratio r, where $r > 0$. Given that $S(2) = 3 \cdot 2$ and $S(4) = 32$, find the values of a and r.

6 The 1st term of a geometric series is 480 and the sum of the first three terms is 390.

Find the possible values of the common ratio.

7 The nth term of a geometric sequence is given by $u_n = 5^{n+1}$

Find a formula for the sum $u_1 + u_2 + u_3 + \ldots + u_n$

8 The sum of the first three terms of a geometric series is $30 \cdot 5$.

If the 1st term is 8, find the possible values of the common ratio.

9 After how many terms will the geometric series:

    $1 + 3 + 9 + \ldots$

exceed $1\,000\,000$?

Exercise 7E Sum to infinity of a geometric series

1 Find the sum to infinity, where it exists, of each geometric series.

   a $6 + 2 + \dfrac{2}{3} + \ldots$ **b** $500 + 100 + 20 + \ldots$ **c** $12 + 18 + 27 + \ldots$

   d $6 - 3 + \dfrac{3}{2} - \ldots$ **e** $4 + 2\sqrt{2} + 2 + \ldots$ **f** $-8 - 6 - \dfrac{9}{2} - \ldots$

2 A geometric series has 1st term 4 and its sum to infinity is $\dfrac{40}{7}$
Find the common ratio of the series.

3 Show that if a geometric series has common ratio $\dfrac{1}{2}$ then its sum to infinity is always twice the 1st term of the series.

4 A geometric series has sum to infinity 50.
Given that the common ratio is $\dfrac{4}{5}$, find the 1st term of the series.

5 In the geometric sequence, $\{u_n\}$, $u_2 = 90$ and $u_5 = \dfrac{80}{3}$
Evaluate $\displaystyle\sum_{r=1}^{\infty} u_r$

6 Find the possible 3rd terms of a geometric sequence whose 2nd term is 300 and whose sum to infinity is 1600.

7 The sum to 4 terms of a geometric series is 15 and the sum to infinity is 16.
Given that the terms of the series are all positive, find its 1st term.

8 Write the recurring decimal $0 \cdot 727\,272\ldots$ as a fraction in its simplest form.

9 $p + (p - 9) + (2p - 42)$ are the first three terms of a geometric series.
Given that the series has a sum to infinity, find its value.

Exercise 7F Expansions of $(1 - x)^n$ and related expansions

1 Write the first four terms of the geometric series for $\dfrac{1}{1 - 3x}$ where $|x| < \dfrac{1}{3}$

2 Write the first four terms of the geometric series for $\dfrac{4}{1 + 2x}$ where $|x| < \dfrac{1}{2}$

> **Hint**   Write the expression in the form $\dfrac{1}{1 - (\ldots)}$ i.e. $\dfrac{4}{1 + 2x} = 4\left(\dfrac{1}{1 - (-2x)}\right)$ etc.

3 Write the first four terms of the geometric series for $\dfrac{5x}{6 + x}$ and state its radius of convergence.

4 **a** Write $\dfrac{7 + 3x}{2 + x - 3x^2}$ as a sum of partial fractions.

    b Hence find a power series expansion for $\dfrac{7 + 3x}{2 + x - 3x^2}$ and write down its range of validity.

Exercise 7G Maclaurin series

 1 Derive the first three non-zero terms of the Maclaurin series for:

    a $f(x) = e^{2x}$ **b** $f(x) = \cos 3x$ **c** $f(x) = \sqrt{1 + 2x}$

    d $f(x) = \ln(1 + x)$ **e** $f(x) = e^{\cos x}$ **f** $f(x) = \sec x$

    g $f(x) = \ln(1 + x^2)$ **h** $f(x) = \sin x^2$ **i** $f(x) = \cos(2x^2)$

    j $f(x) = \tan^{-1} x$ **Hint**   Remember to divide by the factorial in each term.

 2   **a** State the first three non-zero terms in the Maclaurin series for $\sin x$.

    b Hence write down the first three non-zero terms in the Maclaurin series for $x^2 \sin x$.

 3   **a** Find the first three non-zero terms in the Maclaurin series for $\tan x$.

    b Hence find the first three non-zero terms in the Maclaurin series for:

      i $\tan 2x$ **ii** $\tan^2 x$ **iii** $\sec^2 x$.

 4   **a** Write down the first four non-zero terms in the Maclaurin expansion for:

      i e^x **ii** e^{x^2}

    b Hence evaluate $\displaystyle\int_0^1 e^{x^2} dx$ correct to 3 significant figures.

Exercise 7H Using more than one Maclaurin expansion

Example 7.1

Find the Maclaurin series, as far as the term in x^3, for

a $\sqrt{1 + x}$ **b** $\sqrt{1 + 2x}$

a Let $f(x) = (1 + x)^{\frac{1}{2}}$ $f'(x) = \dfrac{1}{2}(1 + x)^{-\frac{1}{2}}$

    $f''(x) = -\dfrac{1}{4}(1 + x)^{-\frac{3}{2}}$

    $f'''(x) = \dfrac{3}{8}(1 + x)^{-\frac{5}{2}}$ (Find the first three derivatives of the expression.)

    $f(0) = 1, f'(0) = \dfrac{1}{2}, f''(0) = -\dfrac{1}{4}$ and $f'''(0) = \dfrac{3}{8}$ (Evaluate $\sqrt{1 + x}$ and the first three derivatives when $x = 0$.)

    $\sqrt{1 + x} = 1 + \dfrac{x}{1!}\cdot\dfrac{1}{2} + \dfrac{x^2}{2!}\cdot\left(-\dfrac{1}{4}\right) + \dfrac{x^3}{3!}\cdot\dfrac{3}{8} + \ldots$

  (The Maclaurin series is $f(0) + \dfrac{x}{1!}f'(0) + \dfrac{x^2}{2!}f''(0) + \dfrac{x^3}{3!}f'''(0) + \ldots$)

    $= 1 + \dfrac{1}{2}x - \dfrac{1}{8}x^2 + \dfrac{1}{16}x^3 + \ldots$ (Evaluate factorials and simplify fractions.)

b $\sqrt{1 + 2x} = 1 + \dfrac{1}{2}(2x) - \dfrac{1}{8}(2x)^2 + \dfrac{1}{16}(2x)^3 + \ldots$ (Replace x with $2x$ using the expansion from part **a**.)

    $= 1 + x - \dfrac{1}{2}x^2 + \dfrac{1}{2}x^3 + \ldots$ (Simplify series.)

1 **a** Write down the first four non-zero terms of the Maclaurin series for

   i e^x **ii** $\sin x$ **iii** $\cos x$

   b Hence find the first four terms in the Maclaurin series for

   i $e^x \sin x$ **ii** $e^{2x} \cos x$ **iii** $\sin 2x \cos 3x$

2 Given that the Maclaurin expansion for $\ln(1 + x)$, for $-1 < x \leqslant 1$, is

$$x - \frac{x^2}{2} + \frac{x^3}{3} - \frac{x^4}{4} + \dots \ ,$$

find a similar Maclaurin expansion for

   a $\ln(1 + 2x)$ **b** $\ln(1 + 3x + 2x^2)$ **c** $\ln\left(\dfrac{\sqrt{1 + 2x}}{1 - 3x}\right)$

3 **a** Show that the Maclaurin series for $\cos 2x$ is given by

$$1 - 2x^2 + \frac{2x^4}{3} - \dots$$

   b Hence find the Maclaurin series for $\cos^2 x$ as far as the term in x^4.

4 **a** Show that $e^{x \ln 2} = 2^x \ \forall x \in \mathbb{R}$

   b Hence find the first four terms in the Maclaurin series for 2^x

Exercise 7I Sigma notation

1 Evaluate

   a $\displaystyle\sum_{r=1}^{5}(3r - 2)$ **b** $\displaystyle\sum_{r=1}^{6}4r^2$ **c** $\displaystyle\sum_{r=3}^{7}(r^2 - r + 2)$

   d $\displaystyle\sum_{j=1}^{4}(3j^3 + 5)$ **e** $\displaystyle\sum_{r=1}^{5}(r! + 2r)$ **f** $\displaystyle\sum_{j=5}^{10}\left(\frac{1}{j + 2} - \frac{1}{j}\right)$

   g $\displaystyle\sum_{r=1}^{6}\ln r$ **h** $\sqrt{\displaystyle\sum_{k=1}^{10}(2k - 1)}$

2 Write in sigma notation:

   a the arithmetic series $1 + 3 + 5 + 7 + \dots + 99$

   b the sum of all the positive integer powers of 2 up to 8192

   c the sum of the first n even numbers

   d the sum of all of the three-digit square numbers

   e the infinite geometric series $8000 + 4000 + 2000 + \dots$

   f the harmonic series $1 + \dfrac{1}{2} + \dfrac{1}{3} + \dfrac{1}{4} + \dots$

   g the geometric series $1 - 2 + 4 - 8 + \dots - 8192$

   h the Maclaurin series for e^x.

3 Let $\{u_n\} = u_1, u_2, u_3, \ldots$ be a sequence.

Write down the expression that should replace the "?" in each equation.

a $\displaystyle\sum_{r=1}^{k} u_r + u_{k+1} = \sum_{r=1}^{?} u_r$

b $\displaystyle\sum_{r=1}^{n} u_r - \sum_{r=1}^{k} u_r = ?$ where $1 < k < n$

4 Let $\{u_n\} = u_1, u_2, u_3, \ldots$ and $\{v_n\} = v_1, v_2, v_3, \ldots$ be sequences and let α and β be constants.

Decide which of the following statements are true and which are false.

a $\displaystyle\sum_{r=1}^{n}(u_r - v_r) = \sum_{r=1}^{n} u_r - \sum_{r=1}^{n} v_r$ **b** $\displaystyle\sum_{r=1}^{n}(u_r v_r) = \sum_{r=1}^{n} u_r \times \sum_{r=1}^{n} v_r$

c $\displaystyle\sum_{r=1}^{n}(u_r)^2 = \left(\sum_{r=1}^{n} u_r\right)^2$ **d** $\displaystyle\sum_{r=1}^{n}(\alpha u_r + \beta v_r) = \alpha\sum_{r=1}^{n} u_r + \beta\sum_{r=1}^{n} v_r$

Exercise 7J Sigma notation using standard results for $\sum 1$ and $\sum r$

1 Evaluate:

a $\displaystyle\sum_{r=1}^{20} r$ **b** $\displaystyle\sum_{r=1}^{50} 3r$ **c** $\displaystyle\sum_{r=1}^{40} (2r + 5)$

d $\displaystyle\sum_{r=1}^{15} (4 - r)$ **e** $\displaystyle\sum_{r=50}^{80} (3r - 7)$ **f** $\displaystyle\sum_{r=64}^{100} (3 - 2r)$

> **Hint** When finding a partial sum e.g. $\displaystyle\sum_{r=k}^{n} f(r)$ (where $k > 1$), use subtraction
>
> i.e. $\displaystyle\sum_{r=1}^{n} f(r) - \sum_{r=1}^{k-1} f(r)$

2 Write in terms of n:

a $\displaystyle\sum_{r=1}^{n} (r + 3)$ **b** $\displaystyle\sum_{r=1}^{n} (5r - 6)$ **c** $\displaystyle\sum_{r=0}^{n} (12 - r)$

d $\displaystyle\sum_{r=1}^{n} \left(\frac{r}{2} + 1\right)$ **e** $\displaystyle\sum_{r=1}^{n} \frac{6 - 2r}{3}$ **f** $\displaystyle\sum_{r=n}^{2n} (r - 4)$

> **Hint** Where the summation includes $r = 0$, i.e. $\displaystyle\sum_{r=0}^{n} f(r)$, make sure you include $f(0)$
>
> in the sum. e.g. $\displaystyle\sum_{r=0}^{n} 1 = n + 1$.

1 Evaluate:

a $\displaystyle\sum_{r=1}^{30} r^2$

b $\displaystyle\sum_{r=1}^{60} 2r^3$

c $\displaystyle\sum_{r=1}^{90} (3r^2 + 5)$

d $\displaystyle\sum_{r=1}^{25} r(r^2 - 2)$

e $\displaystyle\sum_{r=20}^{40} 6r(3 - r)$

f $\displaystyle\sum_{r=41}^{60} \left(r^3 - r^2 - r - 1\right)$

2 Write in terms of n:

a $\displaystyle\sum_{r=1}^{n} (r^2 - 6)$

b $\displaystyle\sum_{r=1}^{n} (4 + r^3)$

c $\displaystyle\sum_{r=1}^{n} 4r(1 - r)$

d $\displaystyle\sum_{r=1}^{n} r(2r^2 + 3)$

e $\displaystyle\sum_{r=1}^{n} (r + 2)(r + 1)$

f $\displaystyle\sum_{r=1}^{n} \left(\begin{array}{c} r + 2 \\ r - 1 \end{array} \right)$

> **Hint** Factorise where possible to ease your working.

3 Given that $\displaystyle\sum_{r=1}^{n} r = \frac{1}{2}n(n + 1)$, find similar expressions for:

a $\displaystyle\sum_{r=1}^{2n} r$

b $\displaystyle\sum_{r=1}^{3n} r$

c $\displaystyle\sum_{r=n+1}^{2n} r$

4 A function is defined on the set of real numbers by $f(x) = x(x^2 + 2)$.

a Show that $\displaystyle\sum_{r=1}^{n} f(r) = \frac{1}{4}n(n + 1)(n^2 + n + 4)$

b Hence evaluate:

i $\displaystyle\sum_{r=1}^{30} f(r)$

ii $\displaystyle\sum_{r=20}^{30} f(r)$

Chapter review

1 Three consecutive terms of an arithmetic sequence are:

$4x, x^2 + 6$ and $x^3 - 9$

a Find the value of x.

b Given that the 1st term of the sequence is 0, find:

i the 20th term

ii the sum of the first 40 terms.

2 **a** Given that $u_k = 11 - 2k, k \geqslant 1$, obtain a formula for S_n where $S_n = \displaystyle\sum_{k=1}^{n} u_k$

b Find the value(s) of n for which $S_n = 21$.

3 A geometric sequence has common ratio $\frac{4}{5}$ and 1st term a where $a > 0$.

a Which term is the first one to have a value less than 1% of a?

b Find the sum of all of the terms in the sequence in terms of a.

4 An arithmetic sequence, $\{u_n\}$, and a geometric sequence, $\{v_n\}$, are such that $u_1 = v_1 = 1$.

Given that the common ratio of the geometric sequence is 3 and that $\sum_{r=1}^{3} u_r = \sum_{r=1}^{3} v_r$,

find the common difference of the arithmetic sequence.

5 Write the first four terms of the geometric series for $\dfrac{2}{3-4x}$ and state its range of validity.

6 **a** If $f(x) = \cos^2 x$, show that $f'(x) = -\sin 2x$.

b Derive the Maclaurin series for $\cos^2 x$ up to the term in x^6.

c Hence, or otherwise, write down the Maclaurin series for $\sin^2 x$ up to the term in x^6.

7 Find the Maclaurin series for $\sec x$ up to the term in x^4.

Hence find a rational estimation of $\sec\left(\dfrac{1}{2}\right)$.

8 **a** The Maclaurin series for $\ln(1+x)$ is:

$$x - \frac{x^2}{2} + \frac{x^3}{3} - \frac{x^4}{4} + \frac{x^5}{5} - \dots$$

Write this series using sigma notation.

b The Maclaurin series for $\cos x$ can be written in the form $\sum_{r=0}^{\infty} (-1)^r \dfrac{x^{2r}}{(2r)!}$

Write the Maclaurin series for $\sin x$ in a similar way.

9 **a** **i** Write down the Maclaurin series for e^x as far as the term in x^3.

ii Find the Maclaurin series for $\tan x$ as far as the term in x^3.

b Hence find the Maclaurin series for $\dfrac{1+\tan x}{e^x}$ as far as the term in x^3.

10 **a** Let $n \in \mathbb{N}$

Show that $\sum_{r=1}^{n} (r+2)(r-2) = \dfrac{1}{6}n\left(2n^2 + 3n - 23\right)$

b Find similar expressions for

i $\sum_{r=1}^{2n} (r+2)(r-2)$ **ii** $\sum_{r=n}^{2n} (r+2)(r-2)$

c Hence evaluate $\sum_{r=50}^{100} (r+2)(r-2)$

8 Matrices

Exercise 8A Addition, subtraction, scalar multiplication and transpose

Example 8.1

A matrix, M, is given by $M = \begin{pmatrix} 5 & 0 & -3 \\ 1 & -1 & 6 \\ 0 & 11 & 2 \end{pmatrix}$

Find M', the transpose of M.

$M' = \begin{pmatrix} 5 & 1 & 0 \\ 0 & -1 & 11 \\ -3 & 6 & 2 \end{pmatrix}$

> To transpose a matrix, switch its rows and columns i.e. row 1 becomes column 1, row 2 becomes column 2 etc.

1 Let $A = \begin{pmatrix} 3 & -1 \\ 1 & 5 \end{pmatrix}$, $B = \begin{pmatrix} 4 & 0 \\ 2 & -3 \end{pmatrix}$, $C = \begin{pmatrix} 5 & 0 & 3 \\ 2 & -7 & 6 \\ 2 & 1 & -4 \end{pmatrix}$ and $D = \begin{pmatrix} -2 & 4 & 5 \\ 3 & 8 & -10 \\ 3 & 2 & -1 \end{pmatrix}$

Evaluate:

a $A + B$ **b** $C - D$ **c** $5C$ **d** $4B - 3A$

e A' **f** $(2B)'$ **g** $2C + D'$ **h** $(D - C)'$

2 Two matrices, P and Q, are given by $P = \begin{pmatrix} 1 & -9 \\ k & 4 \end{pmatrix}$ and $Q = \begin{pmatrix} a & 6 & -1 \\ b & 0 & c \\ 1 & -5 & 0 \end{pmatrix}$

a Given that P is symmetric, write down the value of k.

b Given that Q is skew-symmetric, write down the values of a, b and c.

3 Find the values of x and y, given that $\begin{pmatrix} 4 & x \\ y & -3 \end{pmatrix} + \begin{pmatrix} y & 3y \\ 2x & 8 \end{pmatrix} = \begin{pmatrix} 3 & 6 \\ 17 & 5 \end{pmatrix}$

Exercise 8B Matrix multiplication

1 Let $A = \begin{pmatrix} 2 & 8 \\ -1 & 4 \end{pmatrix}$, $B = \begin{pmatrix} 0 & 3 \\ 5 & 3 \end{pmatrix}$, $C = \begin{pmatrix} 4 & -1 & -2 \\ 0 & 7 & -3 \end{pmatrix}$, $D = \begin{pmatrix} -5 & 1 & -1 \\ -2 & 3 & 4 \\ 3 & 2 & -4 \end{pmatrix}$ and

$E = \begin{pmatrix} 1 & 2 \\ 0 & -2 \\ 6 & 3 \end{pmatrix}$

a Evaluate

     i AB **ii** BA **iii** AC **iv** CD **v** CE

     vi EC **vii** B^2 **viii** D^2 **ix** DC' **x** ABC

b Verify that $(AB)' = B'A'$.

2 Given that $\begin{pmatrix} x & -1 \\ 6 & 4 \end{pmatrix}\begin{pmatrix} y & 0 \\ 5 & -7 \end{pmatrix} = \begin{pmatrix} -2 & 7 \\ 26 & -28 \end{pmatrix}$, find the values of x and y.

3 A matrix, A, is given by $A = \begin{pmatrix} \dfrac{3}{5} & -\dfrac{4}{5} \\ \dfrac{4}{5} & \dfrac{3}{5} \end{pmatrix}$

 a Write down A'.
 b Hence show that A is orthogonal.

4 Given that $B = \begin{pmatrix} \cos x & \sin x \\ \sin x & -\cos x \end{pmatrix}$, show that $B^2 = I \; \forall\, x \in \mathbb{R}$.

5 Let $P = \begin{pmatrix} 3 & -1 \\ 4 & 1 \end{pmatrix}$

 a Show that $P^2 = 4P - 7I$, where I denotes the '2 × 2' identity matrix.
 b Hence write P^3 in the form $\alpha P + \beta I$, where $\alpha, \beta \in \mathbb{Z}$.

6 Let $Q = \begin{pmatrix} -2 & 0 \\ 11 & 5 \end{pmatrix}$

 a Show that Q^2 can be written in the form $mQ + nI$, stating the values of m and n.
 b Find a similar expression for:
  i Q^3 ii Q^4

7 A matrix, M, is said to be **idempotent** if $M^2 = M$.

 a Show that the matrix, A, given by $A = \begin{pmatrix} 4 & -2 \\ 6 & -3 \end{pmatrix}$ is idempotent.

 b Let $M = \begin{pmatrix} a & b \\ c & d \end{pmatrix}$ where b and c are **not both** zero.
  Prove that if M is idempotent then $a + d = 1$.
 c Prove that if the matrix B is idempotent, then so is the matrix $I - B$.

Exercise 8C Determinants of square matrices

1 Let $A = \begin{pmatrix} 2 & -5 \\ 3 & 1 \end{pmatrix}$ and $B = \begin{pmatrix} -3 & 7 \\ -1 & 4 \end{pmatrix}$

 a Evaluate
  i $\det A$ ii $\det B$
 b Verify that
   i $\det(AB) = \det A \det B = \det(BA)$ ii $\det(A') = \det A$

2 Show that the matrix $M = \begin{pmatrix} 8 & -2 \\ 4 & -1 \end{pmatrix}$ is singular.

3 Solve the equation $\begin{vmatrix} 2 & x \\ 3 & x^2 \end{vmatrix} = 2$

4 Two matrices are given by $A = \begin{pmatrix} 1 & -3 & -1 \\ 8 & 0 & 2 \\ -4 & 5 & 4 \end{pmatrix}$ and $B = \begin{pmatrix} 2 & 1 & 6 \\ -4 & 1 & 5 \\ -3 & -2 & -1 \end{pmatrix}$

 a Find $|A|$ and $|B|$.

 b Show that $|AB| = |A|\,|B|$.

5 Find the value(s) of k, given that the matrix $\begin{pmatrix} 4 & k & -1 \\ 2 & -2 & 7 \\ 1 & -k & 1 \end{pmatrix}$ is singular.

> **Hint** Find the determinant by expanding along a row or column.
>
> Remember the matrix of signs $\begin{pmatrix} + & - & + \\ - & + & - \\ + & - & + \end{pmatrix}$

6 Let P and Q be $n \times n$ matrices.

 Show that if P is singular, then so is PQ.

7 Matrix T is given by $T = \begin{pmatrix} \tan\theta & \sec\theta \\ -\sec\theta & -\tan\theta \end{pmatrix}$, $-\dfrac{\pi}{2} < \theta < \dfrac{\pi}{2}$

 Find $|T|$ in its simplest form.

8 Let A be a 2×2 matrix and let k be a constant.

 Prove that $\det(kA) = k^2 \det A$.

9 An **eigenvalue** of a square matrix, A, is a number, λ, satisfying the equation

 $$|A - \lambda I| = 0$$

 Find the eigenvalue(s) of the matrix $A = \begin{pmatrix} 2 & -1 \\ -3 & 4 \end{pmatrix}$

Exercise 8D Inverse of a 2 × 2 matrix

Example 8.2

Find the inverse of the matrix $A = \begin{pmatrix} -5 & -1 \\ 8 & 2 \end{pmatrix}$

$|A| = (-5) \times 2 - (-1) \times 8 = -10 + 8 = -2$

First find the determinant using $\det A = ad - bc$

$\therefore A^{-1} = -\dfrac{1}{2}\begin{pmatrix} 2 & 1 \\ -8 & -5 \end{pmatrix} = \begin{pmatrix} -1 & -\dfrac{1}{2} \\ 4 & \dfrac{5}{2} \end{pmatrix}$

The inverse is $\dfrac{1}{|A|}\begin{pmatrix} d & -b \\ -c & a \end{pmatrix}$

Example 8.3

Let A and B be invertible square matrices.

Prove that if $BAB = I$, then $A = (B^{-1})^2$

$BAB = I$

$B^{-1}(BAB) = B^{-1}I$ •————————————— Pre-(or post-)multiply both sides by B^{-1}

$(B^{-1}B)AB = B^{-1}$

$IAB = B^{-1}$

$AB = B^{-1}$

$ABB^{-1} = B^{-1}B^{-1}$ •————————————— Post-multiply both sides by B^{-1}

$A(BB^{-1}) = B^{-1}B^{-1}$

$AI = B^{-1}B^{-1}$

$A = (B^{-1})^2$ as required.

1   Let $A = \begin{pmatrix} 5 & 6 \\ 3 & 4 \end{pmatrix}$, $B = \begin{pmatrix} 1 & 7 \\ -1 & -6 \end{pmatrix}$ and $C = \begin{pmatrix} 8 & 4 \\ -5 & -3 \end{pmatrix}$

Find

  a A^{-1} **b** B^{-1} **c** C^{-1} **d** $A^{-1}B^{-1}$

  e $B^{-1}A^{-1}$ **f** $(AB)^{-1}$ **g** $(C')^{-1}$ **h** $(C^{-1})'$

2   The matrices P, Q and R are such that $PQ = R$.

  Given that $Q = \begin{pmatrix} 0 & -2 \\ -1 & 3 \end{pmatrix}$ and $R = \begin{pmatrix} 4 & -14 \\ -5 & 11 \end{pmatrix}$, find P.

3   Let A be an invertible 2×2 matrix. Prove that:

  a $|A^{-1}| = \dfrac{1}{|A|}$ **b** $(A')^{-1} = (A^{-1})'$

  c $(A^{-1})^2 = (A^2)^{-1}$ **d** $(A^{-1})^{-1} = A$

4   Let $M = \begin{pmatrix} -2 & 2 \\ 4 & -1 \end{pmatrix}$

  a Show that $M^2 = 6I - 3M$.

  b Hence write:

    i M^3 in the form $pI + qM$ where $p, q \in \mathbb{Z}$

    ii M^{-1} in the form $rI + sM$ where $r, s \in \mathbb{Q}$

5   Let A be a 2×2 matrix such that $A^2 = 3A - 4I$

  a Find the values of p and q such that $A^3 = pA + qI$

  Let B be another 2×2 matrix such that $B = xA + yI$

  b Given that $BA = I$, find the values of x and y.

1 Two matrices, A and B, are given by $A = \begin{pmatrix} 1 & 2 & -2 \\ -1 & 3 & 1 \\ 1 & -2 & -1 \end{pmatrix}$ and $B = \begin{pmatrix} 1 & -1 & -1 \\ 2 & 1 & -2 \\ 0 & 3 & -1 \end{pmatrix}$

a Find A^{-1} and B^{-1}

b Verify that

   i $(AB)^{-1} = B^{-1}A^{-1}$ **ii** $(A^{-1})^{-1} = A$ **iii** $(B')^{-1} = (B^{-1})'$

c Solve this matrix equation.

$$\begin{pmatrix} 1 & 2 & -2 \\ -1 & 3 & 1 \\ 1 & -2 & -1 \end{pmatrix} \begin{pmatrix} x \\ y \\ z \end{pmatrix} = \begin{pmatrix} 10 \\ -7 \\ 7 \end{pmatrix}$$

 2 Two matrices, A and B, are given by $A = \begin{pmatrix} 1 & 0 & 0 \\ 0 & 1 & 0 \\ 1 & 0 & 2 \end{pmatrix}$ and $B = \begin{pmatrix} 2 & 4 & 0 \\ 3 & 1 & 0 \\ -1 & -4 & 1 \end{pmatrix}$

a Find

   i A^{-1} **ii** AB **iii** BA

b Prove that $Q = P^{-1} \Rightarrow PQ = QP$

c Explain why the statement $PQ = QP \Rightarrow Q = P^{-1}$ is false.

 3 Let P and Q be $n \times n$ matrices.

a Prove that $(PQ)^{-1} = Q^{-1}P^{-1}$

b Hence

   i simplify $Q(PQ)^{-1}P$ **ii** show that $(P^2)^{-1} = (P^{-1})^2$

 4 Let X be a square matrix and let I be the corresponding identity matrix.

Given that $\det I = 1$, prove that $\det X^{-1} = \dfrac{1}{\det X}$

Exercise 8F Transformation matrices

 1 Write down the 2 × 2 matrix which represents

a reflection in the x-axis

b reflection in the line $x - y = 0$

c a dilation of scale factor 4 centred at O

d an anti-clockwise rotation of 45° about O

e a clockwise rotation of $\dfrac{\pi}{6}$ radians about O

f an anti-clockwise rotation of $\dfrac{2\pi}{3}$ radians about O.

2 Describe geometrically the transformation represented by each matrix.

a $A = \begin{pmatrix} \frac{1}{2} & 0 \\ 0 & \frac{1}{2} \end{pmatrix}$

b $B = \begin{pmatrix} 0 & -1 \\ -1 & 0 \end{pmatrix}$

c $C = \begin{pmatrix} 0 & -1 \\ 1 & 0 \end{pmatrix}$

d $D = \begin{pmatrix} \frac{1}{2} & -\frac{\sqrt{3}}{2} \\ \frac{\sqrt{3}}{2} & \frac{1}{2} \end{pmatrix}$

e $E = \begin{pmatrix} -1 & 0 \\ 0 & -1 \end{pmatrix}$

f BC

3 **a** Write down the 2 × 2 matrix, T_1, which represents a reflection in the y-axis.

b Write down the 2 × 2 matrix, T_2, which represents a clockwise rotation of 60° about O.

c Hence find the 2 × 2 matrix, T_3, which represents a clockwise rotation of 60° about O followed by reflection in the y-axis.

> **Hint** The images of the points (1, 0) and (0, 1) give the entries in column 1 and column 2 of the transformation matrix respectively.

> **Hint** The transformation represented by matrix A followed by the transformation represented by matrix B can be represented as a single transformation by matrix BA (not AB).

4 **a** Write down the matrix M associated with an anti-clockwise rotation of $\frac{\pi}{4}$ radians about the origin.

b **i** Find M^{-1}, the inverse of M.

   ii State the rotation about the origin with which M^{-1} is associated.

c Write down the matrix X associated with reflection through the origin.

d By evaluating MXM^{-1}, or otherwise, describe the single transformation whose associated matrix could be represented by MXM^{-1}.

5 A triangle has vertices $P(5, 0)$, $Q(0, 2)$ and $R(0, -3)$.

Three transformations are represented by matrices, X, Y and Z and are given by

$X = \begin{pmatrix} 2 & 0 \\ 0 & 2 \end{pmatrix}$, $Y = \begin{pmatrix} -1 & 0 \\ 0 & 1 \end{pmatrix}$ and $Z = \begin{pmatrix} 0 & 1 \\ -1 & 0 \end{pmatrix}$

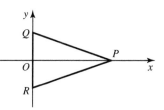

Sketch the image of triangle PQR under the transformations represented by matrix X followed by matrix Y followed by matrix Z.

1 Use Gaussian elimination to solve each system of equations.

a
$$x - 2y + z = 0$$
$$2x + 3y - 5z = 14$$
$$3x - y + 4z = 4$$

b
$$x + y - z = 3$$
$$4x + 5y + z = 10$$
$$-2x + 3y + 2z = -16$$

c
$$2x - y - 3z = 6$$
$$4x + z = 0$$
$$y + 2z = -3$$

d
$$x + 3y + z = 7$$
$$5x - 2y - z = 19$$
$$2x - 11y - 4z = 0$$

2 Show that the system of equations:
$$4x - 2y + z = 10$$
$$3x + y + 4z = 17$$
$$2x + 4y + 7z = 24$$
is redundant.

Hence write the solutions of the system in the form $z = t$, $y = f(t)$, $x = g(t)$.

3 **a** Use Gaussian elimination to reduce the system of equations
$$x + y - 2z = 6$$
$$2x - 3y + z = 2$$
$$3x + y - \lambda z = \mu$$

to upper triangular form.

b Hence state the range of values of λ and μ such that the system has:

i no solutions

ii a unique solution

iii infinitely many solutions.

4 **a** Data collected by scientists during a biological experiment yielded the equations
$$40x - 20{\cdot}1y = 20$$
$$-80x + 40{\cdot}1y = -20$$

Find the values of x and y.

b Given that the system of equations:
$$40{\cdot}1x - 20{\cdot}1y = 20$$
$$-80x + 40{\cdot}1y = -20$$

has solution $x = 40\,000$ and $y = 79\,800$, comment on the system in part **a**.

c How does this affect the scientists' findings?

1 Let $A = \begin{pmatrix} 4 & -5 \\ 2 & -3 \end{pmatrix}$, $B = \begin{pmatrix} -1 & -3 \\ 5 & -12 \end{pmatrix}$, $C = \begin{pmatrix} 2 & -1 & 3 \\ -1 & -2 & 1 \\ 4 & 0 & 1 \end{pmatrix}$ and $D = \begin{pmatrix} 1 & 6 & 0 \\ -2 & 1 & 2 \\ -3 & 2 & 4 \end{pmatrix}$

Find:

a $5A - 2B$ **b** A^{-1} **c** $D' + 3C$ **d** $\det D$

e BA **f** A^3 **g** CD **h** $|AB|$

2 Show that the matrix $\begin{pmatrix} 3x & x+5 \\ x-3 & x \end{pmatrix}$ is invertible $\forall x \in \mathbb{R}$

3 Find the value(s) of k such that the matrix $\begin{pmatrix} 1 & 1 & 0 \\ 0 & k-2 & -1 \\ 1 & 2 & k \end{pmatrix}$ does **not** have an inverse.

4 A transformation matrix, M, is given by $M = \begin{pmatrix} 0 & 1 \\ -\dfrac{1}{3} & \dfrac{2}{3} \end{pmatrix}$

a P, Q and R are the points $(2, 1)$, $(-1, 1)$ and $(-3, 0)$.
Parallelogram $OPQR$ is shown in the diagram.

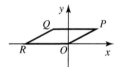

Describe the image of $OPQR$ under the transformation represented by M.

b The image of point A under the transformation defined by M is $(3, 5)$.
Find the coordinates of A.

5 **a** Use elementary row operations to reduce this system to upper triangular form.

$$x - y - z = 6$$
$$2x - 3y + 2z = 6$$
$$3x + y + kz = 15$$

b Solve the system when $k = 8$.

c Explain what happens when $k = -19$.

6 An invertible matrix, X, is given by $X = \begin{pmatrix} a & b \\ c & d \end{pmatrix}$, where b and c are **not both** zero.

The **trace** of X, denoted by $\mathrm{tr}(X)$, is defined by $\mathrm{tr}(X) = a + d$.

a Given that $X^2 = pX + qI$, prove that:

   i $p = \mathrm{tr}(X)$ **ii** $q = -\det X$ **iii** $X^{-1} = \dfrac{1}{\det X}(\mathrm{tr}(X)I - X)$.

b Hence, given that $A = \begin{pmatrix} 3 & -2 \\ -5 & 4 \end{pmatrix}$, write down:

   i A^2 in the form $pA + qI$ where p and q are integers

   ii A^{-1} in the form $\alpha A + \beta I$ where α and β are rational numbers.

9 Vectors

Exercise 9A Direction ratios and direction cosines

1. Two vectors, **a** and **b**, are given by $\mathbf{a} = \begin{pmatrix} 2 \\ -3 \\ -1 \end{pmatrix}$ and $\mathbf{b} = \begin{pmatrix} 7 \\ 0 \\ -2 \end{pmatrix}$

   Find

   a $|\mathbf{a}|$ **b** $|\mathbf{b}|$

   c the direction ratio of **a**   **d** the direction ratio of **a** + **b**

   e the direction cosines of **b**   **f** the direction cosines of **b** − 2**a**

2. P is the point $(3, -6, 1)$ and Q is the point $(1, -1, -3)$.
   Find the direction cosines of $\overrightarrow{PQ}$.

3. A, B, C and D are the points $(1, 3, -1)$, $(3, 7, -3)$, $(3, 10, -5)$ and $(0, 4, -2)$ respectively.
   Prove that $ABCD$ is a trapezium.

Exercise 9B Vector cross product

1. Vectors **u** and **v** are given by $\mathbf{u} = 5\mathbf{i} - \mathbf{j} + 2\mathbf{k}$ and $\mathbf{v} = 8\mathbf{i} - 3\mathbf{k}$.
   Find

   a $\mathbf{u} \times \mathbf{v}$ **b** $\mathbf{v} \times \mathbf{u}$ **c** $\mathbf{u} \times \mathbf{u}$ **d** $2\mathbf{u} \times 3\mathbf{v}$

2. Simplify each expression.

   a $\mathbf{p} \times (\mathbf{p} + \mathbf{q})$ **b** $(\mathbf{p} - \mathbf{q}) \times (\mathbf{p} + \mathbf{q})$ **c** $(2\mathbf{p} - 5\mathbf{q}) \times (\mathbf{p} - 3\mathbf{q})$

3. Triangle ABC has vertices $A(-1, 4, 9)$, $B(2, -2, 1)$ and $C(5, 0, 6)$.
   a Find $\overrightarrow{AB}$ and $\overrightarrow{AC}$ in component form.
   b Hence find the area of the triangle.

4. Vectors **u** and **v** are given by $\mathbf{u} = -\mathbf{i} + 2\mathbf{j} + \alpha\mathbf{k}$ and $\mathbf{v} = \alpha^2\mathbf{i} + 3\mathbf{j} + \mathbf{k}$
   Given that $\mathbf{u} \times \mathbf{v} = 8\mathbf{i} - 7\mathbf{j} - 11\mathbf{k}$, find the value of α.

Exercise 9C Scalar triple product

1. Three vectors, **u**, **v** and **w** are given by $\mathbf{u} = \begin{pmatrix} 4 \\ -3 \\ 2 \end{pmatrix}$, $\mathbf{v} = \begin{pmatrix} 2 \\ 2 \\ -5 \end{pmatrix}$ and $\mathbf{w} = \begin{pmatrix} 1 \\ -1 \\ 6 \end{pmatrix}$

   a Evaluate $\mathbf{u} \cdot \mathbf{v} \times \mathbf{w}$
   b Verify that $\mathbf{u} \cdot \mathbf{v} \times \mathbf{w} = \mathbf{u} \times \mathbf{v} \cdot \mathbf{w}$

2. $ABCD, EFGH$ is a parallelepiped.
   A, B, D and E are the points $(1, 1, 2)$, $(3, 5, -1)$, $(0, 3, 2)$ and $(6, 2, -4)$ respectively.
   Find the volume of the parallelepiped.

   > **Hint** The parallelepiped defined by vectors **u**, **v** and **w** has volume
   > $V = \mathbf{u} \cdot (\mathbf{v} \times \mathbf{w})$

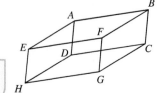

3 Three vectors, **a**, **b** and **c** are given by $\mathbf{a} = \mathbf{i} - 2\mathbf{k}$, $\mathbf{b} = 3\mathbf{i} - \mathbf{j} + 4\mathbf{k}$ and $\mathbf{c} = -5\mathbf{i} + \mathbf{j}$

  a Show that $\mathbf{a} \cdot (\mathbf{b} \times \mathbf{c}) = 0$

  b State the geometric significance of this result.

Exercise 9D Equation of a straight line

Example 9.1

Find the equation of the straight line through $A(2, 1, 5)$ and $B(6, -2, 0)$ in:

a parametric form   **b** symmetric form   **c** vector form.

a $\overrightarrow{AB} = \begin{pmatrix} 6 \\ -2 \\ 0 \end{pmatrix} - \begin{pmatrix} 2 \\ 1 \\ 5 \end{pmatrix} = \begin{pmatrix} 4 \\ -3 \\ -5 \end{pmatrix}$

> Find a direction vector for the straight line.

Straight line is given by $x = 2 + 4t$, $y = 1 - 3t$, $z = 5 - 5t$

> The constant term in each equation comes from the corresponding coordinate of a point on the line (point A). The coefficient of the t-term comes from the corresponding component of a direction vector for the line ($\overrightarrow{AB}$).

b $\dfrac{x - 2}{4} = \dfrac{y - 1}{-3} = \dfrac{z - 5}{-5}$

> Make t the subject of each parametric equation and equate them. Alternatively, remember that a straight line through (x_1, y_1, z_1) with direction vector $\begin{pmatrix} a \\ b \\ c \end{pmatrix}$ is given by $\dfrac{x - x_1}{a} = \dfrac{y - y_1}{b} = \dfrac{z - z_1}{c}$

c $\mathbf{r} = \begin{pmatrix} 2 \\ 1 \\ 5 \end{pmatrix} + \begin{pmatrix} 4 \\ -3 \\ -5 \end{pmatrix} t$

> In vector form, the equation is of the form $\mathbf{r} = \mathbf{a} + \mathbf{u}t$ where $\mathbf{a}$ is the position vector of a point on the line and $\mathbf{u}$ is a direction vector for the line.

 1 Write parametric equations for these straight lines.

  a through the point $(2, 0, -7)$ with direction vector $\begin{pmatrix} 4 \\ 2 \\ -1 \end{pmatrix}$

  b through the points $(1, 1, 5)$ and $(-4, 5, 2)$

  c through the point $(1, 3, 8)$ and parallel to the y-axis

  d given by $\dfrac{x - 2}{3} = \dfrac{y + 1}{-2} = \dfrac{z}{5}$

  e through the point $(7, -2, -3)$ and parallel to the line given by

$$\begin{pmatrix} x \\ y \\ z \end{pmatrix} = \begin{pmatrix} 3 \\ 8 \\ -2 \end{pmatrix} + \begin{pmatrix} -2 \\ 1 \\ 9 \end{pmatrix} t$$

  f through the origin and perpendicular to both $\begin{pmatrix} 3 \\ 0 \\ -2 \end{pmatrix}$ and $\begin{pmatrix} -1 \\ 4 \\ -1 \end{pmatrix}$

2 Write down the equation of the straight line through $A(1, 1, 3)$ and $B(2, 0, -8)$ in
  a symmetric form   **b** parametric form   **c** vector form.

3 A straight line is given by the parametric equations $x = 4 + t$, $y = -5 - t$ and $z = 1 + 3t$.
  a Verify that the point $(1, -2, -8)$ lies on the line.
  b Show that this point also lies on the straight line $\dfrac{x + 1}{2} = y + 3 = \dfrac{z + 4}{-4}$

4 The position of a small asteroid moving through space relative to a fixed origin, O, is governed by the parametric equations $x = 20 - t$, $y = 5 + 2t$, $z = -1 - 3t$, where one unit in the x, y and z directions represents $100\,000$ km and t represents the time, in hours, since the asteroid was first observed.
  a How far away was the asteroid when it was first noticed?
  b How far has the asteroid travelled after 3 days?
  c Calculate the approximate speed of the asteroid in $m\,s^{-1}$, correct to 3 significant figures.

Exercise 9E Intersections of straight lines

1 Two straight lines, L_1 and L_2, are given by:
  $$L_1: \quad x = 3 + 2t, \qquad y = -1 - t, \qquad z = 4 + 3t$$
  $$L_2: \quad x = 1 - 3s, \qquad y = 1 + s, \qquad z = 2 - 5s$$
  a Show that L_1 and L_2 intersect and find their point of intersection.
  b Find the acute angle between L_1 and L_2 to the nearest $0.1°$.

2 Show that the straight lines given by $\dfrac{x - 1}{5} = \dfrac{y + 2}{1} = \dfrac{z - 4}{-2}$ and $\dfrac{x}{3} = \dfrac{y - 6}{2} = z + 3$ do not intersect.

3 Show that the equations $\dfrac{x - 4}{2} = \dfrac{y - 3}{-3} = \dfrac{z + 1}{9}$ and $\dfrac{3x}{-2} = y - 9 = \dfrac{z + 19}{-3}$ represent the same straight line.

4 Two straight lines are given by:
  $$L_1: \frac{1 - x}{3} = \frac{y + 2}{p - 1} = \frac{q - z}{5}$$
  $$L_2: x = 1 + pt, \ y = 3 + t, \ z = -6 + (p - 3)t$$
  Given that L_1 and L_2 intersect at right angles, find the values of p and q.

5 A straight line, L, has equation $\mathbf{r} = (9\mathbf{i} + 13\mathbf{j} - 3\mathbf{k}) + \lambda(\mathbf{i} + 4\mathbf{j} - 2\mathbf{k})$ and passes through point P.
  Given that the point A has coordinates $(4, 16, -3)$ and that AP is perpendicular to L, find the coordinates of P.

6 A particle is moving along a straight line given by the parametric equations:
  $$x = 1 + 2t, \qquad y = 2 - t, \qquad z = -1 + t$$
  where t represents time.
  The point P has coordinates $(1, 2, -5)$.
  a Show that the distance between the particle and the point P at time t is given by
  $$d(t) = \sqrt{6t^2 + 8t + 16}$$
  b Hence, or otherwise, determine the distance between the particle and P when they are at their closest.

Example 9.2

Find the equation of the plane which passes through the point $(-2, -3, 5)$ and contains the line with equation $\dfrac{x}{2} = \dfrac{y-1}{-2} = \dfrac{z+4}{3}$

Two vectors parallel to the plane are:

$$\mathbf{a} = \begin{pmatrix} 2 \\ -2 \\ 3 \end{pmatrix} \text{ and } \mathbf{b} = \begin{pmatrix} -2 \\ -3 \\ 5 \end{pmatrix} - \begin{pmatrix} 0 \\ 1 \\ -4 \end{pmatrix} = \begin{pmatrix} -2 \\ -4 \\ 9 \end{pmatrix}$$

> The direction vector of the line is parallel to the plane since the line lies in the plane. The vector from $(0, 1, -4)$ to $(-2, -3, 5)$ is also parallel to the plane.

$\therefore$ A normal to the plane is $\mathbf{n} = \begin{vmatrix} \mathbf{i} & \mathbf{j} & \mathbf{k} \\ 2 & -2 & 3 \\ -2 & -4 & 9 \end{vmatrix}$

> A normal to the plane is the vector product of two vectors parallel to the plane.

$$= \mathbf{i} \begin{vmatrix} -2 & 3 \\ -4 & 9 \end{vmatrix} - \mathbf{j} \begin{vmatrix} 2 & 3 \\ -2 & 9 \end{vmatrix} + \mathbf{k} \begin{vmatrix} 2 & -2 \\ -2 & -4 \end{vmatrix}$$

> The formula for the vector product is given on the formula list.

$$= \mathbf{i}(-18 + 12) - \mathbf{j}(18 + 6) + \mathbf{k}(-8 - 4)$$

$$= -6\mathbf{i} - 24\mathbf{j} - 12\mathbf{k}$$

$\therefore$ The plane has equation $-6x - 24y - 12z = k$ where $k = \begin{pmatrix} -6 \\ -24 \\ -12 \end{pmatrix} \cdot \begin{pmatrix} -2 \\ -3 \\ 5 \end{pmatrix} = 12 + 72 - 60 = 24$

$\therefore$ The plane has equation $-6x - 24y - 12z = 24$ or $x + 4y + 2z = -4$

1 Find the equations of the planes:

 a through the point $(4, 7, -2)$ with normal vector $3\mathbf{i} - 2\mathbf{j} - \mathbf{k}$

 b through the point $(1, 1, 5)$ and parallel to the plane with equation $8x - 2y + 3z = 9$

 c through the point $(0, 3, 2)$ and parallel to both $\begin{pmatrix} -1 \\ -2 \\ 5 \end{pmatrix}$ and $\begin{pmatrix} 6 \\ 0 \\ 1 \end{pmatrix}$

 d through the points $A(2, -4, 2)$, $B(4, -1, -3)$ and $C(7, -5, 1)$

 e which contains the straight lines $\dfrac{x-2}{1} = \dfrac{3-y}{2} = \dfrac{z-5}{2}$ and $\dfrac{x-7}{1} = \dfrac{y-1}{6} = \dfrac{10-z}{3}$

 f which contains the straight line with equation $\mathbf{r} = \begin{pmatrix} 3 \\ 0 \\ -2 \end{pmatrix} + \begin{pmatrix} 1 \\ -1 \\ 4 \end{pmatrix} t$ and is

 perpendicular to the plane with equation $4x + y - 2z = 12$

 g through $P(7, -4, 3)$ and perpendicular to the line joining $A(2, 0, -1)$ and $B(5, 6, 0)$.

2 Show that the planes with equations $x + 3y + z = 1$ and $2x - y + z = -2$ are perpendicular.

3 The plane with equation $ax + by - 2z = 7$ passes through the points $(5, 1, 6)$ and $(-3, -1, -9)$. Find the values of a and b.

4 Find the shortest distance between the point, P, with coordinates $(3, 5, -4)$ and the plane, Π, with equation $5x - 2y + 3z = 14$.

Exercise 9G Intersections of lines and planes

1 The straight line, L, has equation
$$\frac{x-3}{-7} = \frac{y-2}{-2} = \frac{z-4}{3}$$

and the plane, Π, has equation
$$5x + 2y - 3z = 55$$

a Find the coordinates of the point of intersection of L and Π.

b Find the acute angle, in degrees, between L and Π correct to 3 significant figures.

2 Show that the straight line with equation
$$\begin{pmatrix} x \\ y \\ z \end{pmatrix} = \begin{pmatrix} 0 \\ 1 \\ 3 \end{pmatrix} + \begin{pmatrix} 2 \\ -2 \\ 1 \end{pmatrix} t$$

is parallel to the plane with equation
$$4x + 5y + 2z = 19$$

3 Two planes, Π_1 and Π_2, are given by:
$$\Pi_1: x - 4y + 5z = 17 \text{ and } \Pi_2: 2x + 3y - 7z = 1$$

a Find the equation of the line of intersection of Π_1 and Π_2.

b Calculate the acute angle, in radians, between Π_1 and Π_2 correct to 2 decimal places.

4 Use Gaussian elimination to find the point of intersection of the three planes:
$$x + y - 4z = 0$$
$$2x - y + 5z = 5$$
$$3x + 2y - 7z = 1$$

5 Find the coordinates of the point at which the straight line
$$x - 1 = \frac{9 - y}{2} = z - 5$$

intersects the x–y plane.

6 The plane with equation
$$2x - 3y - 5z = 60$$

intersects the x-axis at point A, the y-axis at point B and the z-axis at point C.
Find the area of triangle ABC.

Chapter review

1 Let $\mathbf{a} = \begin{pmatrix} 3 \\ 1 \\ 4 \end{pmatrix}$, $\mathbf{b} = \begin{pmatrix} -1 \\ 0 \\ 8 \end{pmatrix}$ and $\mathbf{c} = \begin{pmatrix} 5 \\ -4 \\ 2 \end{pmatrix}$

Find:

a $|\mathbf{a}|$ **b** $\mathbf{b} \cdot \mathbf{c}$ **c** $\mathbf{c} \times \mathbf{a}$ **d** $\mathbf{a} \cdot \mathbf{b} \times \mathbf{c}$

e parametric equations for the straight line through $(1, 6, -3)$ with direction vector $\mathbf{b}$

f the equation of the plane through $(9, -2, 5)$ with normal $\mathbf{a}$

g the equation of the plane parallel to $\mathbf{a}$ and $\mathbf{c}$ and which passes through $(4, 1, 2)$

h a symmetric equation for the straight line through O and perpendicular to both $\mathbf{a}$ and $\mathbf{b}$.

2 Find an equation for the straight line which is perpendicular to the plane with equation

$$4x - 2y + z = 10$$

and passes through the point $(-1, 2, 9)$.

3 Two lines, l_1 and l_2, and a plane, Π, are defined by

l_1: $x = 8 - 2t$, $y = 3 + 3t$, $z = 4$
l_2: $x - 6 = \dfrac{y}{-3} = \dfrac{z - 12}{2}$
Π: $x + 2y + 3z = 44$

a i Show that l_1 and l_2 intersect and find the coordinates of their point of intersection.

   ii Find the acute angle between l_1 and l_2 correct to the nearest degree.

b i Find the coordinates of the point where l_2 intersects Π.

   ii Find the acute angle between l_2 and Π to the nearest 0·01 radians.

4 **a** Find the equation of the plane Π_1 which passes through the points A$(0, -1, 3)$, B$(1, 0, 3)$ and C$(0, 0, 5)$.

b Π_2 is the plane through A with normal in the direction $-\mathbf{j} + \mathbf{k}$.

Find the equation of Π_2.

c Determine the acute angle between the planes Π_1 and Π_2.

5 **a** Use Gaussian elimination to show that system of equations

$$x - 3y + 5z = 47$$
$$2x - 2y + z = 14$$
$$3x - 5y + 6z = 61$$

is redundant.

b Hence describe the geometrical significance of this result.

10 Number theory

Exercise 10A Euclidean division

 1 Use Euclidean division to find the quotient and reminder.

   a $93 \div 18$ **b** $129 \div 29$ **c** $-482 \div 103$

   d $9284 \div 98$ **e** $2933 \div (-812)$ **f** $12830 \div 621$

 2 Write 1335 in the form $95a + b$ where $a, b \in \mathbb{N}$ and $b < 95$.

Exercise 10B Converting to base 10

 1 Convert to base 10.

   a 65_8 **b** 1431_6 **c** 22222_3

   d 110100011_2 **e** $7BA_{12}$ **f** $C327_{15}$

 2 What is significant about each sequence of binary numbers?

   a 10, 11, 101, 111, 1011, 1101, 10001, …

   b 1, 100, 1001, 10000, 11001, 100100, 110001, …

   c 1, 1, 10, 11, 101, 1000, 1101, 10101, …

Exercise 10C Converting to other bases

 1 Convert to the given base.

   a 46 to base 5   **b** 260 to base 9   **c** 8932 to base 7

   d 435 to binary   **e** 9925 to base 13

 2 Convert to the given base.

   a 221_3 to base 7   **b** 620_8 to base 11   **c** 8701_9 to base 8

   d $5BA_{12}$ to binary   **e** $9G3C_{18}$ to octal

3 Find the 4th term in this arithmetic sequence and convert it to base 5:

   11111_2, 1201_3, 331_4, …

Exercise 10D Hexadecimal base

 1 Convert to the given base.

   a 1265_{16} to base 10   **b** $2DF2_{16}$ to base 10

   c $7A80_{16}$ to base 6   **d** $19BB_{16}$ to binary

   e 456_7 to hexadecimal   **f** 10100110111_2 to hexadecimal

 2 A geometric sequence of hexadecimal numbers is given.

        1, A, 64, 3E8, …

   Write down the 5th term of the sequence in hexadecimal form.

3 Numerical data stored on a computer hard drive takes up disk space.

Each alphanumeric symbol takes up one unit of disk space.

The binary number 100 111 001 101 011 101 uses 18 units of disk space.

How much disk space would be freed up if this number was stored in hexadecimal form?

Exercise 10E Euclidean algorithm

Example 10.1

a Show that 2565 and 748 are relatively prime.

b Hence find integers, a and b, such that $2565a + 748b = 1$.

a $2565 = 3 \times 748 + 321$

$\quad 748 = 2 \times 321 + 106$

$\quad 321 = 3 \times 106 + 3$

$\quad 106 = 35 \times 3 + 1$

$\quad\quad 3 = 3 \times 1 + 0$

> The Euclidean algorithm starts with 'bigger number = quotient × smaller number + remainder'.

> Algorithm ends when there is a zero remainder.

$\therefore$ The gcd of 2565 and 748 is 1, so 2565 and 748 are relatively prime.

> The gcd is the last non-zero remainder.

b $1 = 106 - 35 \times 3$

> Start by making 1 the subject of the 2nd last line of the algorithm from part **a**.

$1 = 106 - 35 \times (321 - 3 \times 106)$

$1 = 106 - 35 \times 321 + 105 \times 106$

> Again using information from the algorithm, replace 3 with $321 - 3 \times 106$

$1 = 106 \times 106 - 35 \times 321$

> Expand and simplify. Avoid evaluating any of the products.

$1 = 106 \times (748 - 2 \times 321) - 35 \times 321$

$1 = 106 \times 748 - 212 \times 321 - 35 \times 321$

$1 = 106 \times 748 - 247 \times 321$

> Repeat process of substitute, expand and simplify.

$1 = 106 \times 748 - 247 \times (2565 - 3 \times 748)$

$1 = 106 \times 748 - 247 \times 2565 + 741 \times 748$

$1 = 847 \times 748 - 247 \times 2565$

> The process ends when we have an expression in the desired form.

$\therefore a = -247$ and $b = 847$

> State the values of a and b.

1 Use the Euclidean algorithm to find the greatest common divisor for each pair of numbers.

a 1232 and 572   **b** 391 and 276   **c** 578 and 1632

d 5684 and 1085   **e** 374 and 589   **f** 1926 and 5541

2 Show that 1120 and 891 are relatively prime.

> **Hint** Two numbers are said to be relatively prime (or coprime) if their greatest common divisor is 1.

3 Use the Euclidean algorithm to find the highest common factor of 504, 2520 and 3828.

Exercise 10F Extended Euclidean algorithm

1 **a** Use Euclid's algorithm to find the greatest common divisor, d, of 534 and 810.

   b Hence find integers, p and q, such that $534p + 810q = d$.

2 **a** Use the Euclidean algorithm to show that the highest common factor of 1862 and 2277 is 1.

   b Hence write 1 in the form $1862m + 2277n$, where $m, n \in \mathbb{Z}$.

3 **a** Find integers, a and b, such that $3244a + 308b = 4$.

   b Hence find integers, α and β, such that $3244\alpha + 308\beta = 12$.

Exercise 10G Fundamental theorem of arithmetic

1 For each pair of whole numbers:

   i find the prime factorisation of the two numbers

   ii identify their greatest common divisor

   iii calculate their lowest common multiple.

   a 117 and 290   **b** 396 and 216   **c** 378 and 2576

   d 1148 and 2200   **e** 600 and 1540   **f** 784 and 1092

2 **a** Assume that there exists a prime number, P, which is the biggest prime number.

   Now consider the whole number, N, given by

   $$N = 2 \times 3 \times 5 \times 7 \times 11 \times \ldots \times P + 1$$

   i.e. the product of all of the prime numbers plus 1.

   i Assuming P is the biggest prime number, explain why N must be composite.

   ii Assuming P is the biggest prime number, use the fundamental theorem of arithmetic to show that N must **not** be composite.

   b Hence explain the consequences of the results from part **a**.

Chapter review

1 Convert

   a 315_6 to base 10   **b** 3792_{10} to base 5   **c** $4B9D_{16}$ to binary

2 Use the Euclidean algorithm to find

   a the greatest common divisor, d, of 2183 and 6472

   b integers p and q such that $2183p + 6472q = d$.

3 **a** Write 526 and 3862 as products of their prime factors.

   b Hence determine

   i the highest common factor of 526 and 3862

   ii the lowest common multiple of 526 and 3862.

4 Find the prime factorisation of the binary number 101 011 101 010, and write the answer in hexadecimal form.

5 A cycle-hire company hires out ordinary bikes at £27 per weekend and mountain bikes at £41 per weekend. One weekend, bike hire receipts totalled £750.

Let x be number of ordinary bikes hired out and y be the number of mountain bikes hired out.

a Write down an equation relating x and y.

b Solve the equation to find the number of each type of bike hired out.

11 Proof

Commonly used notation

Symbol	Meaning	Examples
$\mathbb{N}$	The set of all **natural** numbers (positive integers)	1, 2, 3, 4, …
$\mathbb{Z}$	The set of all **integers** (positive, negative and zero)	…, –2, –1, 0, 1, 2, …
$\mathbb{Q}$	The set of all **rational** numbers (fractions of two integers)	$\frac{1}{2}$, $-\frac{7}{6}$, 12
$\mathbb{R}$	The set of all **real** numbers	$\sqrt{2}$, $\frac{\pi}{3}$, –5, $4e$
$\mathbb{C}$	The set of all **complex** numbers	$1 - 2i$, $\frac{\sqrt{3}}{2}i$, 9
$\in$	is a member of/belongs to	$11 \in \mathbb{N}$
$\notin$	is not a member of/does not belong to	$\frac{1}{2} \notin \mathbb{N}$
$\exists$	there exists	$\exists n \in \mathbb{N}$ such that $n > 10$
$\forall$	for all / for every	$x^2 \geqslant 0 \ \forall \, x \in \mathbb{R}$
$\Rightarrow$	implies / is sufficient for	$x = 2 \Rightarrow x^2 = 4$
$\Leftarrow$	is implied by / is necessary for	$\cos \theta = 0 \Leftarrow \theta = \frac{\pi}{2}$
$\Leftrightarrow$	if and only if / iff / precisely when	$n! = 24 \Leftrightarrow n = 4$
$\mid$	divides / is a factor of	6|18

Exercise 11A Existential and universal statements

1 Decide whether each statement is existential or universal.

a $x^2 \geqslant 0 \ \forall \, x \in \mathbb{R}$

b $\exists x \in \mathbb{R} \ : 2x + 3 = x^2$

c $2n$ is even $\forall \, n \in \mathbb{N}$

d $4m + 5$ is odd $\forall \, m \in \mathbb{N}$

e $pq \in \mathbb{Q} \ \forall \, p, q \in \mathbb{Q}$

f $\exists z \in \mathbb{C} : z^2 + 5 = 0$

g Let $n \neq 0$. $\frac{m}{n} \in \mathbb{Q}$ for $m, n \in \mathbb{Z}$

h $|\mathbf{u}| \geqslant 0$ for any vector, $\mathbf{u}$

i $|AB| = |A||B| = |BA|$ for any $n \times n$ vectors, A and B.

j $\forall n \in \mathbb{N}, \exists x \in \mathbb{R} : x^2 = n$

 Write each statement using mathematical notation.

a The product of m and n is a natural number for any natural numbers, m and n.

b For any natural number, n, there exists a real number, x, such that $\ln x$ exceeds n.

c The sum of the squares of the natural numbers, a and b, never exceeds the square of their sum.

d For any positive value of ε, there exists an integer, N, such that e^N is less than ε.

e For any vector, $\mathbf{u} \neq \mathbf{0}$, there exists a vector, $\mathbf{v} \neq \mathbf{0}$, such that the scalar product of $\mathbf{u}$ and $\mathbf{v}$ is zero.

f The sum of the moduli of two complex numbers, z_1 and z_2, is never less than the modulus of their sum.

Exercise 11B Logical notation and converse

1 For each statement, say whether it is true or false.

a This month is March $\Rightarrow$ this month has 31 days.

b My lucky number is 7 $\Rightarrow$ my lucky number is prime.

c I live in Glasgow $\Leftarrow$ I live in Scotland.

d $z^2 < 0 \Leftrightarrow z$ is purely imaginary

e $y = 2 \Leftrightarrow y^4 = 16$

f $\mathbf{u} \cdot \mathbf{v} = 0 \Leftarrow$ either $\mathbf{u} = \mathbf{0}$ or $\mathbf{v} = \mathbf{0}$

g I do not own a car $\Rightarrow$ I do not own a vehicle.

h Matrix A is singular iff $|A| = 0$

2 The statements listed below are all true. For each statement:

   i write it using logical notation

   ii write its converse using logical notation

   iii decide whether the converse is true or false.

a If a is positive then the square of a is positive.

b If the product of x and y is zero then either x is zero or y is zero.

c If a triangle is right-angled, then the square on the hypotenuse is equal to the sum of the squares of the other two sides.

d Let $m \neq n$. If m and n are both prime then m and n are coprime.

e Let $p \in \mathbb{N}$. If p^2 is divisible by 3, then p is divisible by 3.

f Let x and y be positive real numbers. If x is greater than y then $\ln x$ is greater than $\ln y$.

g If $f(x) = x^2 + 4x$ then $f'(x) = 2x + 4$

h Let A and B be square matrices. If $AB = BA$, then $(A + B)^2 = A^2 + 2AB + B^2$

Exercise 11C Negation of a statement

1 Write down the negation of each statement.

a $n > 4$ **b** $x = 9$ **c** $y \geqslant 6$

d Some pilots were born in January.   **e** $\forall x \in \mathbb{R}, 2x \in \mathbb{R}$

f $\exists p \in \mathbb{Q} : \sqrt{p} \notin \mathbb{R}$ **g** $\forall z \in \Omega, |z| = 2$

h $\exists x \in \mathbb{R} : \forall y \in \mathbb{R}, xy = 0$ **i** $\forall z \in \mathbb{C} \, \exists y \in \mathbb{C} : \dfrac{z}{y} = i$

2 Write down the negation of each statement.

a $x = 3$ or $x = -5$ **b** $x < -4$ or $x \geqslant 3$

c $0 < y < 1$ **d** n is even and n is a perfect square.

e $x + 2y = 3$ or $x = 0$ **f** $x \in \mathbb{R}$ and $\sqrt{x} \notin \mathbb{R}$

g $\forall n \in \mathbb{N}, n^n \geqslant n!$ and $\ln n^n < n^2$

h $\exists p \in \mathbb{Q}_+ : \forall n \in \mathbb{N}, \dfrac{n}{p} > np$

1 Provide a counter-example to disprove each conjecture.

a Let $x \in \mathbb{R}$. If $x^2 > x$ then $x^3 > x$.

b The product of two prime numbers is always odd.

c Let m, n and p be natural numbers. If $p|mn$ then $p|m$ or $p|n$.

d Let $x \neq y$. If x and y are irrational then $\dfrac{x}{y}$ is irrational.

e If f is an odd function then the graph of $y = f(x)$ must pass through $(0, 0)$.

f If the quadrilateral $ABCD$ is equilateral then $ABCD$ is a square.

g If $\sin P = \dfrac{1}{2}$ then $\cos P = \dfrac{\sqrt{3}}{2}$

h Let A and B be '2 × 2' matrices. If $AB = O$, then $A = O$ or $B = O$.

 2 For each conjecture, decide whether it is true or false. If false, provide a counter-example.

a Let a, b, c and d be natural numbers. If $a > b$ and $c > d$ then $ac > bd$.

b Let A be a 2 × 2 matrix. $A^2 = I \Rightarrow A = I$.

c Let $m, p \in \mathbb{N}$ where p is prime. If p is a factor of m^2 then p is a factor of m.

d Let P_n represent the product of the first n prime numbers. Then $P_n + 1$ is prime.

e Let m and n be natural numbers where $m > n$. Then $m^2 - n^2$, $2mn$ and $m^2 + n^2$ form a Pythagorean triple.

f If p is a prime number then $2^p - 1$ is prime.

g The sum of two irrational numbers is always irrational.

h Let $x, y \in \mathbb{Q}$. The only non-trivial solution of $x + y = xy$ is $x = 2$ and $y = 2$.

 3 A theorem asserts that:

If f and g are even functions then the function h defined by $h(x) = f(x) + g(x)$ is an even function.

a Give a proof of this theorem.

b Disprove the converse of the theorem.

 4 Two statements, P and Q, relating to two distinct natural numbers, m and n, are given by:

P: m and n are square numbers

Q: mn is a square number.

a Show that P is sufficient for Q.

b Show that P is not necessary for Q.

 5 In 1996 the British mathematician Andrew Wiles gave a proof of Fermat's Last Theorem which asserts that:

There are no positive integers x, y and z which satisfy the equation

$$x^n + y^n = z^n \text{ for } n \geqslant 3$$

Two years later, in an episode of *The Simpsons*, an apparent counter-example to Fermat's Last Theorem can be found:

$$3987^{12} + 4365^{12} = 4472^{12}$$

a Use your calculator to investigate this 'counter-example'.

b Explain this paradox.

Example 11.3

Prove by induction that $3^{2n} + 11$ is divisible by 4 $\forall\, n \in \mathbb{N}$.

When $n = 1$, $3^{2n} + 11 = 3^{2(1)} + 11 = 20$ which is divisible by 4.

So, the statement is true for $n = 1$. •────────── Check that the formula works for the smallest value of n, in this case, $n = 1$.

Assume that the statement is true for
$n = k$ (some natural number) i.e. $3^{2k} + 11 = 4p$
where $p \in \mathbb{N}$. •──────────────── State the inductive hypothesis.

Then $3^{2(k+1)} + 11 = 3^{2k+2} + 11$ •────────── Substitute $n = k + 1$

$\qquad\qquad = 3^{2k}.3^2 + 11$

$\qquad\qquad = 9(3^{2k}) + 11$

$\qquad\qquad = 9(4p - 11) + 11$ •────────── Using the inductive hypothesis.

$\qquad\qquad = 36p - 88 = 4(9p - 22)$ •────────── It is important to show that 4 is a factor.

which is divisible by 4, since $(9p - 22) \in \mathbb{N}$.

$\therefore$ If the statement is true for $n = k$, then it is true for $n = k + 1$. Since the statement is true for
$n = 1$, it must be true $\forall\, n \in \mathbb{N}$ by induction. •────────── Give a full explanation to complete the proof.

1 Use proof by induction to show that:

a $5^n - 1$ is divisible by 4 $\forall\, n \in \mathbb{N}$

b $\dfrac{d^n}{dx^n}\{e^{3x}\} = 3^n e^{3x}$ $\forall\, n \in \mathbb{N}$

c $2^n \geqslant n^2 \,\forall\, n \geqslant 4$ Hint $\quad k^2 > 2k + 1 \,\forall\, k > 2$

d $\displaystyle\sum_{r=1}^{n} r(r - 4) = \frac{1}{6}n(n + 1)(2n - 11)$ $\forall\, n \in \mathbb{N}$

e $A = \begin{pmatrix} 2 & -1 \\ 1 & 0 \end{pmatrix} \Rightarrow A^n = \begin{pmatrix} n+1 & -n \\ n & 1-n \end{pmatrix}$ $\forall\, n \in \mathbb{N}$

f $4^n + 6n + 8$ is a multiple of 3 $\forall\, n \in \mathbb{N}$

g $B = \begin{pmatrix} -2 & 9 \\ -1 & 4 \end{pmatrix} \Rightarrow B^n = \begin{pmatrix} 1 - 3n & 9n \\ -n & 1 + 3n \end{pmatrix}$ $\forall\, n \in \mathbb{N}$

h $\dfrac{d^n}{dx^n}\left\{\dfrac{1}{x}\right\} = \dfrac{n!(-1)^n}{x^{n+1}}$ $\forall\, n \in \mathbb{N}$

i $\displaystyle\sum_{r=1}^{n} \frac{2}{3^r} = \frac{3^n - 1}{3^n}$ $\forall\, n \in \mathbb{N}$

j $n^{n-1} > n!$ $\forall\, n \geqslant 3$

2 **a** By considering separately the cases where n is even and n is odd, prove directly that $3n^2 + 9n + 6$ is divisible by 6 $\forall\ n \in \mathbb{N}$.

    b Hence use induction to prove that $n^3 + 3n^2 + 2n$ is divisible by 6 $\forall\ n \in \mathbb{N}$.

3 **a** Simplify $(2n-2)! \times (2n-1) \times (2n)$ where $n \in \mathbb{N}$.

Let $f(x) = x^{\frac{1}{2}}, x > 0$

    b Find $f'(x)$, $f''(x)$ and $f'''(x)$.

    c Prove by induction that, for all natural numbers, n

$$f^{(n)}(x) = \frac{(-1)^{n-1}(2n-2)!}{2^{2n-1}(n-1)!}x^{\frac{1}{2}-n}$$

where $f^{(n)}(x)$ denotes the nth derivative of f with respect to x.

4 **a** Show that $\begin{pmatrix} n \\ r-1 \end{pmatrix} + \begin{pmatrix} n \\ r \end{pmatrix} \equiv \begin{pmatrix} n+1 \\ r \end{pmatrix}$ for $1 \leqslant r \leqslant n$

    b Hence prove by induction that $\sum_{r=0}^{n} \begin{pmatrix} n \\ r \end{pmatrix} \equiv 2^n\ \forall n \geqslant 0$

5 Let $A = \begin{pmatrix} 1 & 0 \\ 2 & -1 \end{pmatrix}$

    a Show that $A^2 = I$, the 2×2 identity matrix.

    b Use the method of proof by induction to show that:

$$A^n = \begin{cases} A, & \text{for } n \text{ odd} \\ I, & \text{for } n \text{ even} \end{cases}$$

6 Let A be an $n \times n$ matrix such that $A = BCB^{\mathsf{T}}$ where B is orthogonal and C is symmetric.

    a Show that A is symmetric.

    b Prove by induction that $A^n = BC^nB^{\mathsf{T}}\ \forall\ n \in \mathbb{N}$.

Exercise 11F Direct proof

1 Prove directly.

    a If n is even, then n^2 is a multiple of 4.

    b The sum of the squares of two odd numbers is always even.

    c If p and q are consecutive even numbers then $pq + 1$ is equal to the square of their intermediate odd number.

    d The sum of any natural number and its cube is always even.

    e $\overline{z^2} = \overline{z}^2\ \forall z \in \mathbb{C}$

    f The product of three consecutive integers is always even.

    g The product of any two real numbers never exceeds half of the sum of their squares.

> **Hint** If n is even, then $n = 2k, k \in \mathbb{Z}$
> If n is odd, then $n = 2k - 1, k \in \mathbb{Z}$

2　**a** Show that $30n^2 + 18n$ is divisible by 4 when:

　　i n is even　　　　**ii** n is odd.

　b Expand $(k + 1)^4$ fully.

　c Hence, and using proof by induction, show that $5n^4 - n^2$ is divisible by 4 $\forall\, n \in \mathbb{N}$.

3　Let m and n be positive integers. Prove by exhaustion that if mn is odd then m and n must both be odd.

4　It is conjectured that every positive integer can be written as a difference of two consecutive prime numbers.

　a Disprove this conjecture by providing a counter-example.

The conjecture is amended and now states that every positive even number can be written as a difference of two consecutive prime numbers.

　b Verify that the new conjecture holds for the first five positive even numbers.

Exercise 11G Proof by contrapositive

Example 11.4

Let n and m be integers.

Use contraposition to prove that $nm = 100 \Rightarrow n \leqslant 10$ or $m \leqslant 10$.

Contrapositive: $m > 10$ and $n > 10 \Rightarrow nm \neq 100$　────────　┌──────────────────────────────────┐
Let $m > 10$ and $n > 10$.　　　　　　　　　　　　　　　　│ The contrapositive of $P \Rightarrow Q$ is $\neg Q \Rightarrow \neg P$ │
　　　　　　　　　　　　　　　　　　　　　　　　　　　　└──────────────────────────────────┘
Then $mn > 100 \Rightarrow mn \neq 100$

Hence the contrapositive is true, which means the statement is also true.

$\therefore\; nm = 100 \Rightarrow n \leqslant 10$ or $m \leqslant 10$

1　For each statement:

　　i write down the contrapositive

　　ii prove the statement is true by proving directly that the contrapositive is true.

　a If the product of two natural numbers is odd then both numbers must be odd.

　b Let $n \in \mathbb{N}$. If n^4 is even then n is even.

　c Let $x \in \mathbb{R}$. If x is irrational then the cube root of x is irrational.

　d Let $z_1 = a_1 + b_1 i$ and $z_2 = a_2 + b_2 i$ be two complex numbers where $b_1 \neq b_2$. Then $z_1 - z_2 \notin \mathbb{R}$.

　e Let $n \in \mathbb{N}$. If $n^3 - 2n^2 + 1$ is even then n is odd.

　f Let $x, y \in \mathbb{R}$. If $x - y$ is irrational then at least one of x and y is irrational.

　g Let f be an injective function. If f is not an odd function then neither is f^{-1}.

　h Let n be a natural number and p be a prime number. If n^2 is divisible by p then n is also divisible by p.

2 Let p be a prime number and n be a positive integer.

It is conjectured that:

p and n are not relatively prime $\Rightarrow n$ is a multiple of p.

a Use contraposition to show that

   i the conjecture is true   **ii** the converse is also true.

b Summarise these results in a single statement.

Exercise 11H Proof by contradiction

Example 11.5

Prove by contradiction that $\sqrt{5}$ is irrational.

Assume that $\sqrt{5}$ is rational, i.e. $\sqrt{5} = \dfrac{p}{q}$ (a fraction in its simplest form) where p and q are

positive integers.   •————————————— | Start by assuming the negation of the statement. |

Then, $5 = \dfrac{p^2}{q^2}$

$\Rightarrow 5q^2 = p^2$ ①

This shows that p^2 is divisible by 5. Since 5 is prime, it follows that p must be divisible by 5. •——— | The prime factor law of squares says that a prime factor of n^2 is also a prime factor of n |

Let $p = 5m$, m a positive integer.

Now, from ①, $5q^2 = (5m)^2$

$$5q^2 = 25m^2$$

$$q^2 = 5m^2$$

This shows that q^2 is divisible by 5. Since 5 is prime, it follows that q must be divisible by 5.

This means that p and q have a common factor of 5. But this is a contradiction as $\dfrac{p}{q}$ was in its

simplest form.

Hence, the assumption must be false.

$\therefore \sqrt{5}$ is irrational.

1 Use proof by contradiction to establish each of the following results.

a $\sqrt{7} \notin \mathbb{Q}$

b $\log_2 5 \notin \mathbb{Q}$

c m^3 is even $\Rightarrow m$ is even

d $x \notin \mathbb{Q} \Rightarrow x + 3 \notin \mathbb{Q}$

e $z^2 \in \mathbb{R} \Rightarrow \mathrm{Re}(z) = 0$ or $\mathrm{Im}(z) = 0$

f Let A be an $n \times n$ matrix. If $A^2 = A$, where $A \neq I$, then A is singular.

g The difference between two odd numbers cannot be an odd number.

h $x \notin \mathbb{Q} \Rightarrow \sqrt{x} \notin \mathbb{Q}$

2 Use the method of *reductio ad absurdum* to prove that if p is a positive rational number, then there exists a rational number q such that $0 < q < p$.

Summary of methods of proof

Method	Description
Direct proof	Showing the truth of a given statement through a straightforward combination of established facts and logical deduction.
Proof by induction	Used to show the truth of a given statement, often relating to the set of all natural numbers. Check for base case, make an inductive hypothesis then prove for the next natural number.
Proof by exhaustion	Used to show the truth of a statement by verifying that it is true for all (a finite number of) possible cases.
Proof by contraposition	The contrapositive of "P $\Rightarrow$ Q" is "not Q $\Rightarrow$ not P". If the statement is true, its contrapositive is true. By directly proving the contrapositive, you can indirectly prove the original statement.
Proof by contradiction	Start by assuming the opposite of the statement you are trying to prove. Through logical deduction from this assumption, arrive at a contradiction. Thus, the assumption must be incorrect, meaning that the original statement is true. Also known as *reductio ad absurdum*.

Chapter review

 1 For the true statement:

This month is January $\Rightarrow$ this month has 31 days.

a write down:

i its converse

ii its contrapositive

iii the converse of its contrapositive

iv the contrapositive of its converse.

b Decide whether each of the above is true or false.

 2 For each statement, decide whether it is true or false.

If it is true, give a direct proof, if it is false provide a counter-example.

a The product of an odd number and the square of an even number is always even.

b $\ln(n!) < n + \sqrt{n} \quad \forall\, n \in \mathbb{N}$

c Let $a, b \in \mathbb{R}$ and $c > 0$. If $a > b$ then $c^a > c^b$.

d Let m and n be positive integers such that $m > n$.

Then $m^2 - n^2$ is a prime number $\Rightarrow m = n + 1$.

3 Prove each statement using mathematical induction.

a $3^n + 1$ is even $\forall n \in \mathbb{N}$

b If $M = \begin{pmatrix} 3 & 1 \\ -4 & -1 \end{pmatrix}$, then $M^n = \begin{pmatrix} 1 + 2n & n \\ -4n & 1 - 2n \end{pmatrix}$ $\forall n \in \mathbb{N}$

c The sum of the first n odd numbers is equal to the square of n.

d If $y = xe^x$ then $\dfrac{d^n y}{dx^n} = (x + n)e^x$ for all positive integers, n.

e $n! > 2^n$ $\forall n \geqslant 4$

f $\displaystyle\sum_{r=1}^{n}(r^3 - 1) = \frac{1}{4}n(n - 1)(n^2 + 3n + 4)$ $\forall n \in \mathbb{N}$

4 Statements P and Q relate to a natural number n and are given by

P: $n^2 - 4n$ is even

Q: n is even.

a Prove that $P \Rightarrow Q$ by considering its contrapositive.

b Hence prove directly that Q is necessary and sufficient for P.

5 Prove by contradiction:

a If $5n^2$ is even then n is even.

b $\sqrt{10}$ is irrational.

c $\sqrt{5} + \sqrt{2}$ is irrational.